STUFF THAT CHANGED THE WORLD

The extraordinary history of ordinary things

Simon Tierney

RED STAG

Published in 2019
RED STAG
(a Mentor Books imprint)
Mentor Books Ltd
43 Furze Road
Sandyford Industrial Estate
Dublin 18
Republic of Ireland

Tel: +353 1 295 2112/3
Fax: +353 1 295 2114
email: admin@mentorbooks.ie
website: www.mentorbooks.ie / www.redstag.ie

A CIP catalogue record for this title is available from the
British Library.

ISBN 978-1-912514-52-6

Acknowledgements

This book wouldn't have been possible without its original incarnation as a radio series. Therefore I want to offer my gratitude to Newstalk 106-108FM, Sean Moncrieff (on whose show it airs) and my producer Claire Collins, for their support over the years. My thanks also to Caroline Clarke for commissioning the series back in 2016.

Thank you to Ger McCarthy, Treasa O'Mahony, Kathryn O'Sullivan and Linda Richardson at Mentor Books for their support, advice and energy in bringing the title to fruition.

My family has been a great support too ... my thanks to John, Fedelma, Stephen, Veronica and Andrew for your constant advice, for reading early drafts and for your general encouragement during the process. Thanks Mum for always carrying that radio around with you! My thanks too to Ingrid Cordeiro for your support and for putting up with me during the project.

I have consulted countless sources for this volume, from books and magazines to old advertisements and films. I must thank all the historians, journalists, sociologists, commentators and others whose work I have read. I have listed these in the bibliography if readers wish to explore their work further.

Finally, a huge thanks to all the listeners of *Stuff that Changed the World* on Newstalk. Your comments and engagement with the series have been enriching, often poignant and frequently hilarious.

For Mum and Dad
:::

CONTENTS

Introduction

The first thing most people do when they get out of bed in the morning is take a pee.

Many people own a receptacle which efficiently and hygienically flushes the waste away from the house. Some people hop into a waterproof cubicle which is designed to spray water on to the body to make it clean. You might use a complex surfactant which magically lathers the hair and body and cleanses it of all dirt and grease.

You might run a sharp blade across your face or over your legs and afterwards rub a special liquid under your arms which plugs the sweat glands in your skin. After this you will pull on an undergarment which holds the breasts in place and offers comfort and support. Or you might draw on a triangular piece of fabric around the groin area which covers the genitals, offers structure and helps prevent the penis from flopping around all day.

You might pop to the kitchen and put pre-sliced bread into a machine which browns it perfectly on each side and even pops up when it's ready. You might even use an electric device which brings water to boiling point within 60 seconds so you can enjoy a cup of coffee.

Before you leave the house you can switch on two large machines. By the time you arrive home these machines will have washed and wrung your dirty laundry and cleaned and dried all your used crockery and cutlery, without you getting your hands wet.

In the space of just a few minutes you will have used ten objects which have completely transformed the world.

This book is an exploration of the extraordinary social history behind the ordinary things in our lives. It is based on my weekly series *Stuff that Changed the World* on Moncrieff on Newstalk radio. When I first started the series I was interested in examining the evolution of the objects and devices which we interact with on a daily basis: the toaster, the dishwasher, the fork, the seatbelt, the kettle. These are sophisticated pieces of technology, but how did they come about? When I scratched the surface I discovered a world of ingenuity ... how the invention of nichrome made a viable heating element in a toaster possible, how a woman had to battle the ingrained misogyny of big industry to convince the world it needed her electric dishwasher and how the addition of a shoulder strap to a seatbelt made cars so much safer to use.

When you gather so many innovations together in one book you begin to see some patterns which help to define what ingenuity is really all about. Although nowadays we take a lot of the inventions discussed in the book for granted, it often required men and women with extraordinary vision to convince others that their idea was a good one in the first place. People are sometimes suspicious of innovation because you need incredible foresight to see what the future already knows. When Clarence Sanders opened the world's first supermarket in 1916 he was ridiculed and told it would never be a success. When Joseph Hanway started using an umbrella in eighteenth century London he was laughed at. John Shepard Barron dreamed of turning a chocolate vending machine into a money vending machine, or 'ATM' as it became known.

The stories in this book are also about the evolution of ideas. Inventions are usually only successful because of trial and error. And sometimes the odd Eureka moment. One of the major problems with early electrical toasters and kettles, for example, was that they continued to burn and boil until the user manually switched them off. When a designer finally managed to integrate automatic shutdown mechanisms, household appliances suddenly became much safer and user-friendly.

Much of the stuff in the book would not have been possible without some landmark leaps of progress. The discovery of artificial carbonation in the eighteenth century, the arrival of electricity in the nineteenth century and the invention of nylon in the twentieth century all contributed to so many other things, from fizzy drinks to street lighting to modern toothbrushes and even running shoes. But perhaps a greater and less obvious influence is at play in the history of these objects: the movement of ideas. Immigration, colonialism and globalisation have played a crucial role in bringing ideas to new places and have helped to marry disparate notions into a coherent whole. When British sailors discovered a fishy brine called *kê-tsiap* on their travels in Asia they brought it back to Europe, added different flavours and anglicised it as ketchup. Sake Dean Mahomed brought a type of Indian head massage called champo to Britain. This idea would eventually coalesce with emerging cleaning agents to form shampoo.

Perhaps the greatest gift many of the things in this book have bestowed on us is that of convenience. Women's lives were transformed by the advancement of household appliances during the early to mid-twentieth century. During times when housework was heavily gendered, appliances such as the washing machine liberated women from the time-consuming drudgery of domestic chores and opened up new avenues of leisure time and work outside of the home.

Everything from the lift to the supermarket to the washing machine is designed to make life easier. But it is the journey that these inventions travelled that tell us not only about the people who designed them, but also about the social and cultural contexts in which they were dreamed up.

I have used many different sources for my research in this volume, from books to movies and museums to advertising. I have also made use of a number of historical newspaper archives from Ireland, the UK and the United States. For more details on these sources please consult the bibliography at the end of the book.

Simon Tierney

▲ AMPEX VIDEO RECORDER VR1000, 1956

THE VIDEO TAPE

'**W**e are on the verge of the video cassette age,' warned a column in the *Munster Express* in May 1979, just a few short months before Ireland's first video rental store, Xtra Vision, opened its doors in Ranelagh in 1980. 'Cross channel, they reckon there are about 100,000 sets fitted with video cassette facilities, and while they were originally used for recording programmes for later viewing, now there are a number of firms specialising in supplying sex films for viewing on your own TV set. Nobody can dictate to you what you can or can't watch in the privacy of your own house and they're taking full advantage of it. How long before we have this in the island of saints and scholars?'

This element of freedom, the ability to watch what you wanted, made video irresistible. But the columnist was very perceptive. Pornography played a crucial role in developing the fledgling home video industry in the late '70s. *Debbie Does Dallas* sold 50,000 copies in the United States when it arrived on VHS in 1979, making it the most successful porn movie of its time. Adult film executives were quick to recognise that home video could bring them a large

▲ DEBBIE DOES DALLAS, 1979

9

audience beyond traditional theatrical releases. 'Repeatedly in the history of reproductive technologies, pornography has been one of the earliest and most commercially successful forms of content,' writes Lucas Hilderbrand in *Inherent Vice*. 'Pornography was the most prominent content available for pre-recorded cassettes in the late 1970s.'

This period witnessed a format war between the two pioneers of home video, Sony and JVC. But why did JVC's VHS system win out over Sony's Betamax? Cost and the length of the recordable format played a role but pornography also contributed enormously to JVC's success. Sony turned up their nose at smut and decided not to allow pornography on its format. Big mistake. This allowed JVC to gain an upper hand. By 1980, 50 per cent of the home video market was in pornography and so JVC were milking it. 'Despite a two-year head start by Sony, by 1980 the VHS market share had reached 70 percent. At that point it was game over,' argues Franz Johansson in *The Click Moment*. 'Sony never recovered, and in 1988 they officially shut down the Betamax line. Killed off by *Debbie Does Dallas*.'

Video was first introduced in the 1950s as a way to record live television broadcasting. Charles Ginsburg of the Ampex Corporation designed the world's first video cassette recorder (VCR) in 1956, the VRX-1000. A complex machine using rotating heads to record on two-inch magnetic tape, it was the size of an

▲ DOUGLAS EDWARDS, CBS, 1950S

industrial washing machine and took up half a room. CBS bought the machine for $50,000 (almost half a million dollars in today's money) and used it for the first time on November 30th of that year. The network recorded a live broadcast of *Douglas Edwards and the News* in New York City and then replayed the same broadcast a few hours later in Los Angeles.

This solved a major headache for TV networks. Before the launch of the tape recorder, news programmes went out as live.

Because of America's multiple time zones, the programmes were often broadcast at unsociable times. If the evening news went live at 6pm in New York, then it was inconvenient for viewers to watch the same programme at 3pm in California. This new technology allowed broadcasters to record, delay and rebroadcast at any time they wished.

Kinescope technology had existed before video tape but it was time consuming and of poor quality. It involved the filming of a TV monitor during a live broadcast. This film was then developed over the course of several hours and rebroadcast for a different time zone. It was archaic and a far cry from the instant results of video tape. The VCR was considered to be such a revolutionary shift in technology that Ampex received a special prize at the 1957 Emmy awards. Soon the other networks caught on and videotape recording became the norm for the future of television.

The development of home video recorders was stunted by Hollywood studios and television networks. They feared it would decapitate their business. 'Hollywood executives were caught off guard when Sony released its consumer-targeted Betamax video recorder in 1975,' writes Peter Decherney in *Hollywood's Copyright Wars*. Rentable videos didn't yet exist so these machines allowed consumers to record movies and programmes directly off their TV sets. This was a copyright conundrum. It was also feared that tape recording would damage the networks' advertising sales. Advertising is sold to specific demographics watching TV at a particular time of the day. Video tape recording took control out of the hands of television executives. This led to numerous court cases regarding copyright and fair use.

Eventually, however, the home video would become king when Hollywood executives began to realise that the new technology could actually benefit them. For example, the profits that Disney earned from releasing its old classics on home video during the 1980s helped it to fund its future.

Home video had become a more viable and lucrative business model when a man named Andre Blay had the pioneering idea of bringing movies into people's homes. Blay ran Magnetic Video, a video recording company in Michigan. After the introduction of Betamax in 1976, Blay wrote to all the Hollywood studios requesting permission to license their films on videos, which he would then sell

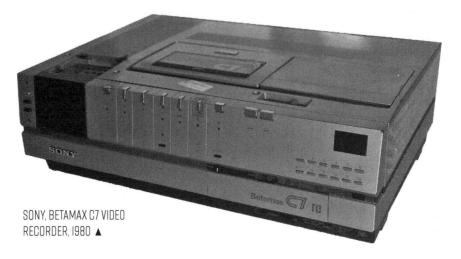

SONY, BETAMAX C7 VIDEO
RECORDER, 1980 ▲

commercially. Twentieth Century Fox was the only studio that agreed to sign a deal. 'Magnetic Video guaranteed half a million dollars a year in exchange for the non-exclusive rights to fifty films. Fox was to receive a royalty of $7.50 for every tape unit sold,' writes Frederick Wasser in V*eni, Vidi, Video: The Hollywood Empire and the VCR.*

Among the conditions in this early foray into home movie distribution was that the films must be over two years old. *Patton, The Seven Year Itch* and *The French Connection* were among the first titles made available to consumers. Although the parameters of the deal were limited, this was the first time that people could actually go out and buy their favourite movies and watch them at home in their own time. However, Blay's video cassettes were prohibitively expensive at between $50 and $70 per tape. This was the only way he could recoup his costs on the punishing contract he had signed with Fox. Despite the cost there was almost immediate and overwhelming demand for Blay's tapes. Fox suddenly recognised the vast potential in Blay's vision and bought him out for $7 million. The home video market had well and truly landed.

The video shop was an institution for a certain generation. Almost every week movie buffs would pop in and browse the aisles, eagerly examining the latest releases to have arrived. It had its own smell, like a library but with the added aroma of magnetic tape and sweat from well-thumbed cassette cases. The disappointment at finding that the new release you came in for was rented out already, the 'Be kind, rewind' sticker on the tapes, the express return letterbox

... all these elements contributed to an experience, something that is now sadly lost, as consumers turn to digital platforms like Netflix. Blockbuster, the major American video store conglomerate, shut its doors in 2013 while Xtra Vision closed for business in Ireland in 2016. Yet for over thirty years the video rental industry thrived. But how did it begin?

George Atkinson, an American entrepreneur involved in everything from the distribution of adult movies to films of boxing matches, was curious about the potential of Andre Blay's new video sales business. Because of the high cost of videos, many in the industry saw home video as being similar to the vinyl record business, that rich collectors would build libraries of movies in their homes. He wondered if there might be a demand for renting these videos at low cost as opposed to buying them at considerable expense. In a much later interview, with the *Los Angeles Times* in 1987, he remarked, 'I said: "You listen to Beethoven or the Beatles over and over again. You don't watch Burt Reynolds over and over".' He placed an ad in the *Los Angeles Times* to test the waters. It simply read, 'Videos for rent'. He included a coupon for readers to post to him. One thousand readers contacted him within a week. He now knew there was a demand, but he didn't have any supply.

In order to purchase stock, Atkinson began charging a $50 membership fee to his new rental store, The Video Station. Members could then rent a movie for $10 per night. This was still expensive for the late 1970s, but it was significantly cheaper than buying individual cassettes.

The Video Station, the world's first video rental shop, was situated on Wilshire Boulevard in LA and opened for business in December 1977. Atkinson's business model became so successful that he eventually franchised the Video Station to hundreds of affiliated branches around southern California, and spawned imitators all over the world. As late as 2005, the year of Atkinson's death, there were 24,000 video rental shops across the United States, pulling in a collective revenue of $8 billion per year. Within ten years the industry would be dead.

Someone should tell he

2 THE TOOTHBRUSH

In 1947 the toothpaste company Colgate launched an advertising campaign with the tagline, 'Someone should tell her (but nobody does)'. The ad featured two gentlemen whispering privately about a despondent woman in the foreground. Advertisers had begun to recognise that an effective way to push sales of hygiene products was to shame consumers into buying them. The copy read, 'Many a girl never finds out why her romances fizzle out. That's because, much as they dislike Oral Offence, people just can't bring themselves to tell a girl she is guilty of it'. This advertisement speaks volumes about mid-twentieth century obsessions with cleanliness (not to mention misogyny).

The history of the toothbrush is one of great invention and whimsy. In his book *The Excruciating History of Dentistry*, James Wynbrandt describes all manner of tools and concoctions that were employed by the Ancients in a desperate attempt to look after their teeth. 'Hippocrates recommended using a small ball of wool moistened in honey, and then a rinse of dill, aniseed, myrrh, and white wine,' he writes. Pliny the Elder always seemed to be an expert on everything and, of course, he gave his two cents on the matter in *Natural History* (77AD) by recommending a mix of honey and powdered dogs' teeth as a toothpaste. Fresh as dog breath. Thanks Pliny.

One of the earliest toothbrushes was the *miswak*, still used in some Muslim

◄ THE MISWAK

communities to this day. The *miswak* is a stick taken from the fibrous bark of the Salvadora persica tree. The bark is cut off the end of a very thin branch, revealing a besom-like interior which is ideal as a natural toothbrush. The opposite end of the stick may have been pointed and used as a toothpick. The Salvadora persica contains fluorine and other antibacterial agents which help to protect the teeth. It also has a sweet pungent aroma which freshens the breath. According to *Hadith* the Prophet Mohammed said, 'If I had not thought it hard for my followers or the people, I would have ordered them to clean their teeth with *miswak* for every prayer. I use *miswak* so relentlessly that it seems as if my teeth (or my gum) will be scraped off'.

It is believed that the bristle toothbrush emerged during the Tang Dynasty in China, some time during the eighth century. These would have been bamboo sticks pierced with tiny holes containing the bristles of the cold climate hog of northern China and Siberia. There is written evidence that Chinese monks were using toothbrushes made out of ox bone and horse tail hair by the thirteenth century. Indeed, it was this horsehair model that was eventually brought back to European shores and became popular during the sixteenth century. The horsehair brush was softer on the gums than harsh pig bristles. Napoleon's toothbrush, which is still preserved in the Wellcome Collection in London, was made with horsehair bristles. It has a highly decorative silver gilt handle and is engraved with the letter 'N'.

William Addis is often credited with making the world's first mass produced toothbrush. According to the *Journal of the History of Dentistry*, Addis had been imprisoned in London in 1769 for his participation in a riot. While in jail he had saved a bone from dinner, bribed a guard to provide him with some bristles and glue and then put it all together as a makeshift toothbrush. He later patented his

▲ NAPOLEON'S TOOTHBRUSH, SILVER-GILT HANDLE AND BRISTLES MADE OF HORSEHAIR. WELLCOME COLLECTION design and began mass producing his brush to great success from 1780. Badger hair was used for his pricier brushes while the handles were made from the bones of bullocks, boiled down and then cut into strips. Later on, wood was used for the handles. Eventually, his company would become Wisdom Toothbrushes, a market leader to this day.

Eighteenth and nineteenth century toothbrushes were painful and often dangerous to use. Many people, particularly those who couldn't afford bristle brushes, relied instead on the rubbing rag. This was a piece of cloth used to rub ash or coal dust across the teeth in an effort to agitate the filth and polish your gnashers.

The toothpick was in widespread use too. Until fairly recently, toothpicks were often brought to your table in a restaurant along with your bill. This seldom, if ever, happens now. The idea of picking meat out of one's teeth in front of other diners is perhaps something which has become less and less socially acceptable over time. In the 1830 book *Dental Surgery*, Dr Samuel Fitch says that 'the toothpick should have a place in every gentleman's pocket and every lady's toilet, and should be always used after every meal'. An advertisement in the *Los Angeles Herald* in January 1889 gives an unpleasant insight into the perils of bristle toothbrushes and why people were put off by them. The ad itself is promoting a new 'felt tooth polisher' which is being endorsed by a dentist who says, 'I have no hesitation in saying that anyone who uses it for one week will never go back to the miseries of loose bristles and constantly wounded gums'. Felt obviously never took off as a major alternative to animal bristles but something else did: nylon.

The DuPont Company invented nylon in 1937. They quickly realised that this new material could solve some of the inherent problems associated with the traditional toothbrush. Animal hair and bristles fell out repeatedly and they took a long time to dry. This meant that bacteria grew, causing mouth infections. Nylon bristles were stiff and didn't go soft once they became wet. In 1940, Dupont, along with Wisdom Toothbrushes, launched Dr West's 'Miracle Tuft' toothbrush, the world's first toothbrush with nylon bristles, setting the standard for the future of dental care.

People now had toothbrushes, but what was being used as a toothpaste? After the invention of the first commercially available toothbrushes at the end of the eighteenth century 'dental creams and powders became popular and were sold in porcelain jars into which entire families would dip their damp toothbrushes,' according to Kerry Seagrave, author of *America Brushes Up*. Often the flavours and ingredients of late nineteenth century toothpastes were different to today's. For example, London's Science Museum has an 1890's pot of 'tooth soap', manufactured by S.J. Weston. The central ingredients are myrrh and borax. Myrrh was celebrated for its supposed antiseptic qualities, while borax helped to foam the mixture in the mouth.

One of the most successful toothpastes in the second half of the nineteenth century in America was Sozodont, created by a New Yorker named William Henry Hall. It was bright red in colour and came in a large glass bottle. Hall was a master salesman and Sozodont was widely advertised across the country. In one ad, the product was endorsed by 15 clergymen. The support of the church was clearly seen as key to boosting toothpaste sales. However, the product was 37% alcohol. 'In 1897, the financial manager of the Sozodont firm had to testify before Congress to assure the government that consumers were not purchasing the product as a tax-free form of liquor. Sozodont also contained abrasive and acidic ingredients that gradually destroyed tooth enamel,' according to the *Smithsonian*.

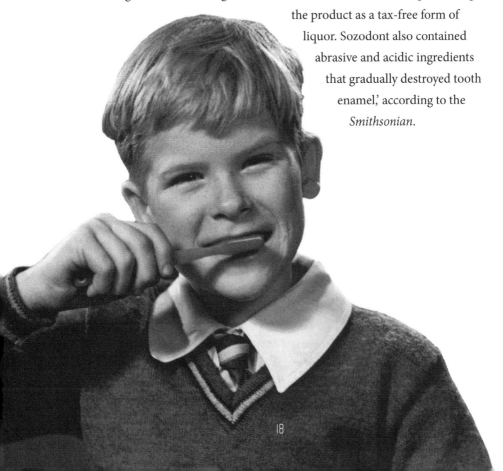

Eventually, the focus on toothpaste shifted from cosmetic appearance to the ability to prevent tooth decay. When the brand Crest introduced fluoride into their product in 1955, this became the key ingredient for toothpaste manufacturers from then on.

Easy Tomato Ring Men Like!

1st Prize bridge -party Pie!

1948 GELATIN SALAD ADVERTISEMENT ▲

KNOX SPARKLING GELATINE

THE SALAD

The modern salad has become so complicated in its ingredients and so endlessly customisable that it is ripe for satire. Meg Ryan's convoluted salad orders in the classic 1989 comedy *When Harry Met Sally* come to mind. Harry teases her when he says, 'You're high maintenance but you think you're low maintenance … "I'll begin with the house salad, but I don't want the regular dressing. I'll have the balsamic vinegar and oil, but on the side". There is now such a wide definition of what a salad actually is, that it obliges us to return to its origins in order to understand what on earth it's all about.

The word 'salad' derives from the Latin *salata*, meaning 'salted'. In Ancient Greece and Rome salted and oily vegetables such as lettuce were part of the common diet. Lettuce, perhaps the most common ingredient in the history of salad, has been a controversial vegetable through the ages. The word comes to us from the Latin *lactuca*, meaning milk, because of the white liquid that seeps from the stem of its wild variety. This milky liquid was considered a soporific. It was for this reason that it generated a reputation as an antidote to sexual urges. Dioscorides, the surgeon in Nero's army, prescribed lettuce to his soldiers when they pined after their wives. He felt a good dose of greens would ward off unwanted 'libidinous images'.

The ancients believed in the curative power of salad. The Emperor Augustus was said to have had a statue of a romaine lettuce erected after it cured him of illness. Marcus Claudius Tacitus, another Roman Emperor, was described as 'a great friend to lettuce'. It was seen not just as a powerful sleep agent and tamer of the libido, but also as an aid to digestion. Hippocrates played an important role in the early promotion of raw vegetables. In fact, the popular cos lettuce enjoyed by consumers across Europe to this day, gets its name from the island of Kos in Greece, where the great physician was born. Hippocrates argued that vegetables should be consumed at the beginning of a meal, to aid digestion. He was persuaded that raw vegetables cleared the system, making way for the heavier foods that came later in the meal. Perhaps this is why salads often feature as a starter in modern culinary traditions. The Romans, on the other hand, ate their salad at the end of a meal, to make them dozy before bed.

The Elizabethans had a fear of lettuce. It was suggested by some that its soporific qualities and supposed ability to inhibit sex could be very frustrating to couples and that even if children were born of lettuce-eating parents, they would end up 'peevish' and 'foolish' as a result.

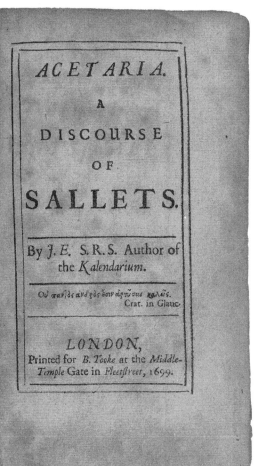

The modern salad crept into the English diet after the publication of gardener John Evelyn's *Acetaria: A Discourse on Sallets,* in 1669. He described salad as 'a particular composition of certain crude and fresh herbs, such as usually are, or may safely be eaten with some acetous juice, oil, salt, etc.'. Once again, salad was seen not simply as a food, but as a source of almost spiritual wholesomeness. He argued that lettuce 'kindly nourishes, mitigates pain; besides the effect it has upon the morals, temperance and chastity'. Evelyn's book was the first in the English language devoted to the promotion of salad.

◄ ACETARIA, A DISCOURSE ON SALLETTS, 1669.
WELLCOME COLLECTION

There are two particular salads which became famous in America due to the contribution of immigrant culture: coleslaw and Caesar salad, both of which have now become widely enjoyed dishes throughout the Western culinary world. Dutch immigrants brought coleslaw to New York in the eighteenth century. They called it 'koolsla.' 'Kool' is Dutch for cabbage while 'sla' means salad. In fact, Dutch colonists introduced cabbage to North America for the first time when they started growing it on Long Island. 'The recipe for the salad was changed in the US, with the primary addition being mayonnaise, which was lacking from the original Dutch cabbage salad, which was seasoned solely with vinegar,' writes Nicoline Van Der Sijs in *Cookies, Coleslaw, and Stoops: The Influence of Dutch on the North American Languages*. It's no surprise that the Americans added mayonnaise to coleslaw, a condiment with European origins but which discovered its mass appeal in the US.

Mayonnaise and salad have been bedfellows for a long time, but the condiment's history goes right back to the 1750s. At that time the British occupied the island of Menorca, off the coast of Spain. In 1756, the Duke de Richelieu invaded the town of Mahon with a force of 15,000 Frenchmen and the British surrendered soon after. Richelieu, who was famous for his interest in nudism, often eating in the nip, ordered his chef to whip up a celebratory meal. The chef set about cooking a delicious banquet but had run out of fresh cream for his sauce. Instead, he mixed olive oil with eggs, perhaps inspired by local aioli recipes. The Duke loved it and christened it 'Mahonnaise' in tribute to his victory at Port Mahon. Over time this came to be called *mayonnaise* and has been accompanying sandwiches and salads ever since.

Caesar Cardini was an Italian immigrant operating a popular restaurant called Caesar's Place in Tijuana, on the Mexican border with the United States. During the 1920s, Caesar's had become a popular watering hole for Hollywood movie stars. In an attempt to escape prohibition, they would pop across the border for a night of debauchery. After the July 4th celebrations in 1924, Caesar's customers were demanding food in the early hours of the morning when he discovered that he was almost out of provisions. In a moment of desperate inspiration Caesar concocted a meal of romaine lettuce, parmesan cheese, egg, olive oil and Worcestershire sauce. This was a heavier than usual salad and the boozy Yanks lapped it up. At that time, it was unheard of to eat a salad as a main course but

Caesar's innovation changed that.

In his biography of Julia Child, Bob Spitz discusses the influence of Caesar on the great future chef when she visited his Tijuana establishment. 'It was a sight to behold for a fourteen-year-old with a serious appetite. Fifty years later she could envision the artfully flamboyant process. "I can see him break two eggs over that romaine and roll them in, the greens going all creamy as the eggs flowed over them. Before then salads were considered rather exotic, definitely foreign, probably Bolshevist, and, anyway, food only for sissies". Eventually the Caesar salad moved across the border, becoming popular in the United States and beyond. In 1948 Caesar took out a patent on his special egg dressing. Cardini's Original Caesar Dressing is still sold all over the world today. Caesar's Restaurant and Bar also still exists in Tijuana, serving up the original salad to its customers. By 1953 the Caesar salad was globally famous. In that year the International Society of Epicures in Paris declared it to be 'the greatest recipe to originate from the Americas in 50 years'.

Gelatin salads flourished right up to the 1970s and '80s. But their genesis goes all the way back to the beginning of the century when the brand Jell-O began promoting these products. These salads consisted of vegetables and meat suspended in a colourful and wobbly congealed mass of gelatin. Gelatin was cheap and contained protein. 'Jell-O salads, it turned out, were the perfect place to hide leftovers and stretch the contents of a meagre cupboard,' writes Allie Rowbottom in *JELL-O Girls: A Family History*. After World War Two gelatin salads came to typify the sophisticated suburban home and fed into

◄ GELATIN PORK SALAD

the new trend for pre-prepared food. This, of course, was made possible by the sudden proliferation of home refrigerators. 'There was hardly anything a 1950s housewife could do that would impress her guests more than to serve a beautiful molded Jell-O dish,' according to the *Oxford Encyclopaedia of Food and Drink in America*.

Every type of mould existed to create these translucent monstrosities. Lime cheese salad consisted of a seafood mix encased in a ring of sweet gelatin. Other favourites included lamb chops suspended in green jelly and sauerkraut and onion in lemon flavoured gelatin. 'On warm summer days that call for cool cooking ... see how a jellied seafood mold ... will rouse the most languishing appetite,' reads the salad section of a 1970 Betty Crocker Cookbook. Gelatin salads seem bizarre to modern consumers, but they have become icons of their time, a brief chapter in the ancient history of salad.

▲ GENE KELLY IN SINGIN' IN THE RAIN, 1952

4
THE UMBRELLA

'**I**'m dancing, I'm singing, in the rain,' sings Gene Kelly in the classic 1952 musical. What always amused me about his performance is that he uses his umbrella for everything except protecting himself from the actual rain. The umbrella is a prop, something to dance around and play with. A gentleman's accessory. In fact, much of the history of the umbrella has nothing to do with rain at all. Its origins are in Egypt where it offered protection from the sun.

However, it was in nineteenth century Britain that the umbrella developed its iconic status as 'a carefully crafted sign of high distinction, to be carried not only as a shield against the wet, but as a mark of fashion and good taste,' writes Marion Rankine in *Brolliology*. However, during the second half of the twentieth century, much like the trilby hat, the umbrella witnessed a decline in its symbolic importance as something which had been prized for its beautiful craftsmanship.

Now, more often than not, it is a mass-produced, cheaply bought and purely functional tool, something throwaway that people feel little affection for. The miserable image of half broken umbrella spokes, protruding from a city's rubbish bins in the aftermath of a downpour, comes to mind. Every year over 10,000 brollies are lost or abandoned across London's public transport system, only 2% of which anybody bothers to reclaim. Whereas in previous centuries there were small artisan umbrella makers across Europe, with people taking great pride and ownership of their brolly, now 98% of the world's entire umbrella stock is produced in China.

Umbrellas are thought to have originated in Ancient Egypt and Assyria (northern Iraq and south-eastern Turkey), as early as the eighth century BC. They were used symbolically as a way to signify authority. 'Many Egyptian pictures dating hundreds of years before the bas-reliefs of the Assyrians, portray the umbrella as an appendage of a priest or prince,' writes Albert Henry Longhurst in *The Story of the Stupa*. These would have been made of wood and designed in a conical shape. They were not simply used to protect royalty from the sun, but also to evoke the idea of heaven covering the sacred. The Greeks and Romans also used umbrellas to signify authority, but their use appears to have died after the fall of the Roman Empire.

Perhaps it makes sense that China produces the majority of the world's umbrellas nowadays since it also played an important role in their ancient traditions. The character for 'umbrella' in Chinese is the san (傘), which is a pictorial representation of the object itself. Early umbrellas were made from silk with a bamboo shaft and were an indicator of social rank. Later the canopies came to be made with paper and were lacquered with wax or tongyou, a special plant oil, to make them waterproof. During the Ming Dynasty (fourteenth to seventeenth centuries), different coloured umbrellas signified various ranks. 'The Governor General carries two large red silk umbrellas; the four highest Mandarins carried black models with a red silk lining and three flounces,' says Rankine.

During the Middle Ages the umbrella was reintroduced in Italy. It was here that it got its name. The Italian word *ombra* means 'shade'. An umbrella followed the Pope during processions and even became part of the insignia of the Vatican. The *Sede Vacante* is one such symbol. It features Saint Peter's keys to the kingdom of heaven. On top of the keys is a yellow and red umbrella. 'This is said to denote the absence of the pope and the temporary government by the Camerlengo,' explains Anura Guruge in *The Next Pope*. 'As with the canopies that were erected above the cardinals' thrones at conclaves prior to 1978, this umbrella could indicate that the church was being governed, temporarily, on a collegiate basis by the College of Cardinals.'

Thomas Coryate, the great seventeenth century English travel writer, was the first to use the word umbrella in the English language. In his travelogue, *Coryate's Crudities,* he writes, 'They commonly call in the Italian tongue umbrellaes, that is, things that minister shadow unto them for shelter against the scorching heate of the Sunne'. In the text he describes these peculiar accessories, made of leather, and often used by men while riding horses, with the shaft attached to their thighs to keep them secure.

Although it had been known as a parasol in France, meaning 'defence against the sun', a Paris manufacturer, by the name of Jean Marius, developed a light, foldable umbrella by 1710, which was waterproofed for rainy weather. He was a purse merchant and had noticed that the ladies attending his shop were getting their wigs wet on rainy days. He knew they wouldn't want to carry a large umbrella with them so he set about designing one that was discreet and easy to carry. His 'folding pocket parasol-umbrella' was an instant hit. For the first time an umbrella's canopy could be folded down into a slim rod. The shaft was made in three jointed sections which meant that the entire apparatus could be disassembled into something discreet that could be carried in a bag (although it sounds like it took quite a while to put up and put down.) Louis XIV was taken with this invention and granted Jean Marius a five-year royal patent, which meant that every single umbrella manufactured in France carried his trademark until 1715. It became known as a *parapluie* (*pluie* is French for rain) to distinguish it from its sunny counterpart, the parasol.

Although women were already using umbrellas in England by the eighteenth century, it was still considered socially unacceptable and even effeminate for men to use them. The philanthropist Jonas Hanway attacked this gender divide when he returned to England after his travels in Persia, where they were popular. 'He was the first man who ventured to dare public reproach and ridicule by carrying an umbrella,' wrote

▲ 1871 ENGRAVING OF JONAS HANWAY WITH HIS INFAMOUS UMBRELLA

William Sangster, himself an umbrella manufacturer, in 1855. Some thought it ungodly to defy heaven's tears. Coachmen decried them, imagining themselves going out of business if the fad took hold. On one occasion a hansom cab driver attempted to run Hanway over. Hanway suddenly found a new use for his umbrella, as a weapon for whacking the unsuspecting cabbie. Men were afraid to carry an umbrella in England, and 'anyone doing so was sure to be hailed by the mob as "a mincing Frenchman"', according to Walter Thornbury's history of London. Despite this initial opposition to Hanway's umbrella, his trend had started to take hold by the time of his death in 1786.

In 1830, England's first dedicated umbrella shop, James Smith & Sons, opened in Bloomsbury in London. It is still in operation to this day. Rankine argues that the popularisation of the umbrella in the early nineteenth century was part of a wider trend for fashion accessories. 'Luxury objects that had previously been the preserve of the ultra-rich were democratised through the production of cheaper, but still high quality imitations, and flaunted as signs of status and refinement,' she says. When the parasol belonging to the Maharajah of Najpoor was put on display at the Great Exhibition of 1851 it caused quite a stir and lent an exotic allure to the umbrella. William Sangster recalled, 'The ribs and stretchers, sixteen in number, divided the umbrella into as many segments, covered with silk,

© Jorge Royan

▲ JAMES SMITH & SONS, ONE OF THE WORLD'S OLDEST UMBRELLA SHOPS, OPENED IN 1830 exquisitely embroidered with gold and silver ornaments'. All this led to a thriving umbrella manufacturing industry in London, where almost 1,500 people were employed in the trade by the mid-nineteenth century.

Earlier umbrella ribs were made with whalebone and could be as heavy as two kilograms. However, in 1852 the umbrella

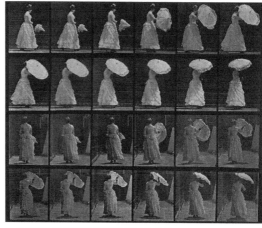

▲ WOMAN OPENING AN UMBRELLA, 1887. WELLCOME COLLECTION

underwent a revolution. Samuel Fox was looking for a way to use up surplus wire from his corset making business. From this humble beginning he was inspired to introduce steel spokes to the umbrella. This was a lighter and more durable material than whalebone and set the standard for the umbrellas we still use today. Gingham and alpaca had also become the canopy of choice. Alpaca, introduced by Sangster, was much cheaper than silk and more durable than cotton. By 1855, four million alpaca Fox umbrellas had been sold, establishing the umbrella as an essential gentleman's accessory. Sangster later claimed in his book *Umbrellas and their History*, 'We ... claim our share of distinction in being patronized for the last few years by the esteemed lady of Abraham Lincoln, President of the United States'.

Perhaps the last great innovation in umbrella technology came in 1928 in Berlin when Hans Haupt invented the telescopic umbrella. Haupt had an injury which caused him to use a walking stick. Carrying both a walking stick and an umbrella was burdensome so he set about designing a telescopic function which would allow him to easily minimise the umbrella and keep it in his bag. He called the resulting umbrella a 'knirp'. This is German for 'tot' or 'squirt', emphasising its diminutive size. His invention was so successful that 'knirp' became a generic synonym for umbrella in Germany. It is also the name of an entire umbrella company, still producing Haupt's design to this day.

THE COFFIN

An article in the *New York Times* in 1868 reported on an astonishing new invention, designed to mitigate a common fear during the nineteenth century. 'A German gentleman, advanced in years, named Franz Vester, at present a resident at Newark, recently received a patent for a safety coffin, designed so as to provide a way of escape to those who might be buried during suspended animation.' In nineteenth century Europe and America, taphophobia, the fear of being buried alive, was rampant during a time when medical practitioners were less adept at reaching a conclusive diagnosis of death.

▲ THE DEAD ALIVE BY HENRY WIGSTEAD, 1784. WELLCOME COLLECTION

As late as the 1920s, evidence of premature burial persisted. Author Jan Bondeson recounts the memories of a gravedigger during the Great Depression in the United States. During the exhumation of bodies in a graveyard, he recalled that it had 'been a horrible experience to see how many of the corpses had been buried alive by mistake ... there were gashed and broken foreheads from pounding the coffin lids, torn fingernails and desperately contorted faces that the young gravedigger never forgot'. Popular stories of the nineteenth century, such as Mary Shelley's *Frankenstein*, perpetuated people's fears. In Edgar Allen Poe's 1844 short story *The Premature Burial*, the narrator is so obsessed with falling into a cataleptic coma, and therefore being presumed dead, that he had a special tomb designed which would allow him a way to escape from his coffin, an idea not dissimilar to Vester's a quarter of a century later.

Vester's invention consisted of a two-foot square chimney structure to deliver oxygen into the coffin below. The chimney housed a little ladder to allow the prematurely buried to climb out of their tomb. Provisions were also made in the event that the interred were too weak to climb out. 'Under the head is a receptacle for wine and refreshments,' reported *The Spectator* in 1868. 'A spring inside enables the occupant to ring a bell,' which would presumably both alert and terrify any passers-by. Vester was so convinced of his solution to premature burial that he performed a live demonstration to a crowd of onlookers in New

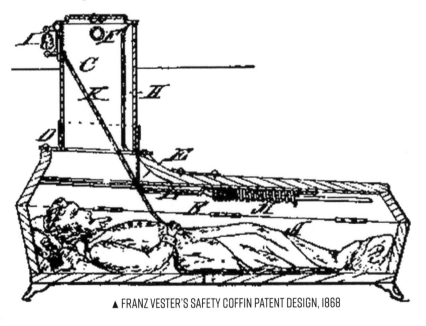

▲ FRANZ VESTER'S SAFETY COFFIN PATENT DESIGN, 1868

York. After an hour he emerged from his grisly tomb 'with no more perceptible exhaustion than would have been caused by walking two or three locks under the hot sun'.

Some of the earliest coffins were wooden and were developed during the Naqada Period in Ancient Egypt, from 3800 BC. Before this, corpses were simply wrapped in cloth or reeds and buried in a pit. Early Dynastic Period (3000 BC) coffins were made of wood panelling and featured architectural detailing resembling the facade of a palace. Coffins developed with the increased importance of religious rituals during burial. The sarcophagus, an above-ground stone tomb, was used in both Ancient Egypt and Greece. It derives its etymology from the Greek words *sarco* (flesh) and *phagus* (eater). 'The earliest types of these burial vessels, according to ancient scholars Pliny and Theophrastus, were made out of Assius stone,' writes Douglas Keister in *Stories in Stone*. 'Because of its caustic properties, this stone reduced the body to bone in a matter of weeks.' Later sarcophagi were designed to preserve a mummified corpse rather than destroy it, but the grisly flesh-eating description persisted.

Excavations of Roman London have revealed that lead was an important material in the coffin making business. This is a soft metal that could be easily manipulated. A number of lead coffins in the collection of the Museum of London, including that of a child, are highly decorative with scallop shell and ribbon patterning. To achieve this level of detail, a sand box would have been built. A real shell would then be used to make an impression in the sand. The lead would have been melted down and poured gently into the sand box and allowed to cool, leaving the memory of the sea shell intact.

During the Middle Ages in England, people were buried in wooden or stone coffins. 'If the person was wealthy enough, the coffin could have been made specially and buried with the person. In an early Tudor example, a coffin was described as being 'waxed' for Richard Hunne, a rich London merchant,' explains Christopher Daniell in *Death and Burial in Medieval England, 1066 to 1550*. On the other hand, the poor were buried in a 'reusable parish coffin'. This would have held the body during the funeral, but once the burial took place, the body would have been removed and buried in a shroud. This was a practice which the Holy Roman Emperor Joseph II (Marie Antoinette's brother) reintroduced in 1784, in a measure designed to save on resources. His 'economy coffin' had a hinged

trap door in the base. As it was lowered into the grave, the undertaker released
the hinge and the body dropped. The coffin was then removed and set up for the
next burial. The Viennese were appalled and riots ensued until Joseph eventually
retracted the policy.

The word coffin derives from the Latin *cophinus,* meaning 'basket'. It was first
used in English, in a burial context, in the 1520s. During the Plague in London
in 1665, the Lord Mayor, William Lawrence, issued strict orders regarding burial.
In an attempt to stop the spread of infection from rotting corpses, those who had
died of plague were to be buried 'at least six feet deep'. This was the beginning of
the 'six feet under' tradition, although nowadays graves tend to be shallower than
this.

In the eighteenth and nineteenth centuries, the proliferation of medical
schools in Britain and America demanded an increase in the availability of
cadavers for students to study anatomy. The supply of executed criminals,
delivered directly from the gallows, simply didn't meet demand. The stealing of
corpses from coffins became commonplace, at first by medical students and later
by professional body snatchers. 'This shift was at first gradual. Bribing corrupt
sextons with a few pence from their allowance, slowly adapted into paying a
bodysnatcher to bring a cadaver to the back door of the anatomy school', explains
Suzie Lennox in her history of this grisly enterprise. The 'resurrection men', as
they became known, first had to locate a new grave, because only fresh cadavers
could be sold to the schools. Taller corpses were particularly prized because the
cadavers sold by the inch. Under the cover of night, they carefully dug down at
the head end of a grave, using wooden spades (metal ones were too noisy and
attracted attention). The lid would then be crowbarred open. 'Standing aside to
let the corpse gasses escape, they could then begin to place ropes either around
the corpse's head or under its armpits', explains Lennox. 'On the count of three
the cadaver could be pulled free of the coffin ... stripped of its grave clothes and
squashed into a sack.'

In the nineteenth century, the city of Baltimore, in the United States, was a
major centre of body snatching due to the presence there of six medical schools.
The resurrection men pickled the cadavers in barrels of whiskey to preserve
them and stifle the stench. Once the body had been successfully delivered to the
customer, the putrid whiskey was sold off to saloons as a cheap beverage for their

customers. This delicious concoction was fondly known as 'rotgut.'

Undertakers turned to more durable materials such as iron and lead, sealed and secured under lock and key, to deter the bodysnatchers. Iron cages were devised to entomb coffins. Graveyards such as Glasnevin Cemetery in Dublin, opened in 1832, were designed with watch towers so that guards could survey the grounds and apprehend the wily resurrection men. A high profile case in 1878 inspired entrepreneurs to find better solutions to body snatching. The body of an Irish millionaire by the name of Alexander Turney Stewart was stolen by snatchers from St. Mark's in New York in that year. Stewart had grown up in Lisburn but had made his fortune as a retailer in America. 'The stealing of A.T. Stewart's body started a host of inventors into a new line of labor, the object being to prevent the repetition of so horrible a crime,' reported the *New York Times* in 1882.

One innovative solution was introduced by Philip K. Clover, who invented the Torpedo Coffin. 'It was, in essence, a trap or spring gun, installed inside the coffin. When the grave robber attempted to remove the body from the coffin, the trigger was sprung, sending a ball or buckshot upwards, and, hopefully, into the body of the thief,' writes Wayne Fanebust in *The Missing Corpse*. According to a January 1881 edition of an Ohio newspaper, 'On Monday night three body snatchers, while attempting to rob a grave near Gann, this county, met with a fatal accident. While excavating the grave the picks came in contact with a torpedo, which exploded, killing one of the ghouls'.

Today, the coffin continues to be the burial choice of many, contributing to the multi billion-dollar funeral industry. Although we only see them at funerals, they fill our landscapes, six feet under, a testament to an ancient tradition that continues to entomb and honour the dead.

JEAN SHRIMPTON AT THE MELBOURNE CUP IN 1965 ▲

THE miniskirt

British supermodel Jean Shrimpton shocked the world in 1965 when she turned up at the Melbourne Cup, one of the most prestigious horse racing events in the world. Her crime? Wearing a miniskirt. The *Sun* newspaper in Australia decried, 'There she was, the world's highest-paid model, snubbing the iron-clad conventions at fashionable Flemington in a dress five inches above the knee, NO hat, NO gloves, and NO stockings!'

The 22-year-old Shrimpton, with heartthrob boyfriend Terence Stamp as her escort, was in Melbourne to judge the Fashion in the Field prize and to promote a new line of fabric for DuPont. Because her dress designer, Colin Rolfe, had received only a limited amount of the material with which to make a number of dresses, he decided to draw the hem up higher than usual. His attempt to make a little go a long way had far reaching consequences for the fashion industry. In her autobiography Shrimpton writes, 'When we arrived at the racecourse it didn't take long to realise I had committed the most terrible faux pas. The Melbourne women, in stockings, hats and long white gloves, were pointing at me and glaring … I was surrounded by cameramen, all on their knees like proposing Victorian swains, shooting upwards to make my skirt look even shorter'.

Back in Blighty, the *Liverpool Echo* reported on the incident as if she had committed a mortal sin. 'Shrimp is unrepentant,' ran the headline. 'On the eve of her departure for home she said, "I don't give a damn what people wear. They should be allowed to please themselves. I've always worn short skirts, and while I'm young I'll go on wearing them. They are obviously not suited for fat old women, and when I get old I won't wear them either"'.

The miniskirt shocked and, indeed, changed the world because it represented a bold rejection of what was considered acceptable for a woman to wear. Before the 1960s women were generally encouraged to dress similarly to their mothers. Now, a new post-war generation was experimenting with a fresh sense of identity. 'Sixties women, as a whole, were more assured than many of their predecessors,' explains Sheila Hardy in *Women of the 1960s*, 'they wanted to have a career, be independent, and enjoy themselves'. The miniskirt was a product of the Swinging Sixties and came to symbolise a small but significant chapter in women's liberation.

British fashion designer Mary Quant is often credited as the driving force behind the popularity of the miniskirt. In fact, she coined the term, naming it after her favourite car, the Mini Cooper. One of her motivations in developing the skirt was her desire to showcase the legs and ankles of the female body, to celebrate them as something to be seen and admired, rather than hidden behind layers of fabric. In her autobiography, Quant writes, 'The Sixties mini was the most self indulgent, optimistic "look at me, isn't life wonderful" fashion ever devised. It expressed the sixties, the emancipation of women, the pill and rock 'n roll'.

This all played out in Quant's small shop called Bazaar on the King's Road in Chelsea. Her customers demanded that she draw the hemline higher and higher, and she obliged, pushing the limits of sartorial acceptability into ever more audacious territory. Then came the inevitable backlash: 'city gents in bowler hats beat on our shop window with their umbrellas shouting "Immoral!" and "Disgusting!" at the sight of our miniskirts'. Some countries banned them, but Quant remained defiant. In an interview with the *Guardian* newspaper in 1967 she said, 'In European countries where they ban miniskirts in the streets and say they're an

▲ THE BRITISH FASHION DESIGNER MARY QUANT IN FRONT OF BUCKINGHAM PALACE, JUNE 16, 1966

invitation to rape, they don't understand about stocking tights underneath'.

The miniskirt also caused outrage in Catholic Ireland. In 1967 the *Evening Herald* described it as 'the controversial fashion introduced from Britain'. Yet another heathen import from our former overlords. One of the earliest mentions of the miniskirt in the Irish media comes from an editorial in the *Irish Times* from May 1966. The writer lamented the fact that 'women continue to submit to fashions that seemed designed by the enemies of womankind. Could it be that leading couturiers, those who set the fashions, are men who do not like women, and who enjoy making money while they think out new ways of making their victims ridiculous. "Nasty, brutish and short," said Hopper of human life under conditions of war. Might he not say the same thing about the mini-skirt?'

A rather frazzled reader of the *Evening Herald* wrote a letter to the newspaper in February 1967, alarmed after noticing a guest wearing a miniskirt on the *Late Late Show* the previous Friday. He lamented, 'As a man I feel very concerned at these modern fashions ... I firmly believe that a female who wears these miniskirts for a couple of years, must stand the risk of getting purpley coloured goose pimples and hairy legs'. The miniskirt also caused controversy at Carysfort College in Dublin in 1973 when 600 trainee teachers went on strike at the institution's ban on miniskirts. While it isn't clear whether their action paid off, their efforts tell us a great deal about how the miniskirt became a rallying point for women in Ireland to demand greater freedoms.

The miniskirt continues to ignite fierce controversy in conservative societies today. In 2014 the Ugandan government, notorious for its strict social policies, introduced new Anti-Pornography Laws, which included within its remit the banning of miniskirts. Simon Lokodo, Uganda's Minister of State for Ethics and Integrity, vowed to arrest women wearing skirts that stopped above the knee line. He claimed that this move would help to apprehend women who were threatening 'the moral fibre of the country'. When the law was passed, Ugandan newspapers reported on women being stripped of their miniskirts in an act of public shaming, by men purportedly 'helping' the police. This led to protests spearheaded by the End Miniskirt Harassment Coalition.

This invention of the 1960s evidently continues to be a focal point for the rights of women to this day.

▲ CHARCOAL IRON. IMAGE: VINCENT DE GROOT

THe IRON

'**T**o be able to iron properly requires much practice and experience,' advises Mrs. Beeton in her 1861 *Book of Household Management*. 'After wiping down her ironing table, the laundry maid should place a coarse cloth on it, and over that the ironing blanket, with her stand and iron rubber; and having ascertained that her irons are quite cleaned and of the right heat, she proceeds with her work.' The attention to detail in these instructions offers a unique insight into the laborious process of ironing laundry during the nineteenth century. The iron, as we recognise it today, appears to be a simple device, yet it has gone through an extraordinary evolution to reach its potential.

The three most common irons during the Victorian period were the sad or flat iron, the box iron and the charcoal iron. The sad iron, first wrought in the Medieval period, took its name from the Middle English meaning of 'sad' which meant *solid*. Mrs. Beeton mentions multiple irons in the above quotation because they took so long to heat and once removed from the fire they began to cool immediately. A six-pound iron could take up to an hour and a half to reach the required temperature for ironing. Some sad irons could be 15 pounds in weight. The laundry maid would alternate her irons in and out of the fire or stove as they cooled.

The box iron, introduced by the Dutch, offered a clever solution to the ever-increasing number of irons required in a busy household. 'An iron slug was shaped to fit the hollow body, which had either a hinged or sliding heel or top for access. A housewife needed only one iron and two slugs, which were heated alternately during the ironing,' says Olive Sharkey in *Old Days, Old Ways*.

The charcoal iron required more work and preparation but stayed hot for longer. This was a hollow iron, with a hinged lid, that could hold burning coals. Venting holes along the top allowed oxygen into the chamber to keep the coals smouldering. These could be dangerous to use as smoke escaped through the vents near the user's hand. Eventually charcoal irons came with little chimneys which diverted smoke away from the instrument, saving hands and preventing the laundry from smelling charred. One German-made charcoal iron, the Dalli, began using smokeless fuel in the 1890s. An advertisement declared, 'Marriage troubles avoided by using the Dalli box iron. Heat and work of the ironing day makes wife and servant irritable ... double the work in half the time'. According to London's Science Museum, which houses an 1850 Cannon Charcoal Iron, a 'bellows pumped air inside to keep the charcoal burning for longer, but the temperature was difficult to control'.

Initially the handles of all these devices were made of iron, just like the body. Thick oven gloves were required to use them. In 1870, detachable handles were introduced by Mary Florence Potts, of Iowa. These could be attached after the sad iron was heated on the stove. One advertisement for 'Mrs. Potts Cold Handle Sad Irons' claimed to have 'Detachable walnut handles ... Require no holder or cloth ... Do not burn the hand'. Meanwhile, right into the early twentieth century, rural homes which were not connected to electricity sometimes used petrol, paraffin or gas irons. A petrol iron featured a bulbous container on the back which held the fuel. It was lit with a match and a valve could control the temperature.

In the Victorian period, ironing in a large country house took place in a designated

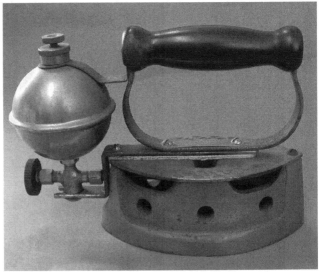

▲ A PETROL IRON, EARLY TWENTIETH CENTURY. AUCKLAND MUSEUM

ironing room. It was hot, sweaty and exhausting. As Bill Bryson explains in *At Home*, 'The irons were heavy in themselves and it was necessary to press down with great force to get the desired results. But they also required delicacy and care because there were no controls, so it was easy to scorch fabrics. Heating irons over a fire made them sooty too so they had to be constantly wiped down'.

Homemade starch was often concocted in the kitchen to add stiffness to shirt collars. This would then leave a residue on the iron which needed to be sandpapered off after use. Mrs. Beeton recommended adding a little candle wax to the starch mix to prevent this from happening. In *The Lady's Maid: My Life in Service*, Rosina Harrison recalls watching her mother dealing with the sheer volume of ironing equipment involved in a big house. 'There was an attachment that was fitted to the kitchen stove with two ledges which held the irons. This was kept red hot and Mum must have had eight to ten irons on it at any one time. There was one little round one with which she polished the gentlemen's collars and the starched dress shirt fronts till they shone.'

Have we always been so concerned about creased clothing or is this an activity dreamed up by the Victorians? In fact, the history of ironing goes all the way back to Ancient Greece. Ironing may have had a dual purpose in times gone past, to not only smooth fabric, but also to kill parasites nesting in clothing and bed linens. The Greeks used a 'goffering iron' which was a cylindrical bar which would be heated and then rolled over fabric to create pleats. The Romans were known to use a mangle to break down creases, much like a similar instrument would be used to wring excess water from wet laundry in later times (see Chapter 23, The Washing Machine).

The Vikings used a curious device called a *Sleksje* or 'linen smoother'. Discovered in the graves of Viking women, these were round wood or glass objects in the shape of an inverted mushroom which could be pressed over creases. Some were hollow, allowing for the insertion of a hot coal which would help the ironing process. Slickstones, as they later became known, were used in Europe right up until the nineteenth century and were particularly prized for small jobs when the tedious process of heating a sad iron wasn't deemed necessary.

By the late nineteenth century, every conceivable type of ironing attachment had been invented and refined, from the hat iron for smoothing the brim of a gentleman's bowler to the goffering iron for pressing cuff frills. The nineteenth century goffering iron, sometimes called an Italian iron, featured a long cylindrical piece of metal in the shape of a missile, set on a stand. A red hot poker was then inserted into the hollow missile to heat the device up. Frilly cuffs were wrapped around the cylinder to smooth out their creases. In a direct reference to the goffering iron, Charlotte Brontë mentions 'Italian-ironed double frills' in her novel *Shirley*.

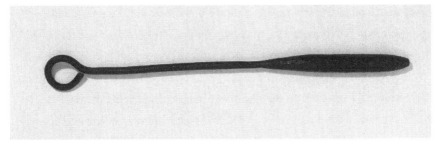

▲ GOFFERING IRON, CA 1850. © VICTORIA AND ALBERT MUSEUM, LONDON

The ironing industry shifted dramatically in 1883 with the introduction of the world's first electric iron. Henry Seely of New York had developed a cordless iron that was heated on a metal stand which, in turn, was connected to an electrical source. Once the iron was heated it was removed from the stand and put to use. The drawback, of course, was that it began to cool immediately and needed to be continuously reheated on the electric stand.

The first successful electric iron was invented by Earl Richardson, a meter reader with the Ontario Electric Company in California. Unlike Seely's iron, this one remained attached to the electrical source by a cord. Richardson engineered his device in such a way that there was a concentration of heating elements at the pointy part of the iron, allowing the device to smooth out creases around buttonholes. He called this the 'hotpoint'. It was so successful that by 1912 he had established the Hotpoint Electric Heating Company. Hotpoint remains a market leader to this day.

Richardson recognised that in order for home electrical appliances to flourish, the power companies needed to provide a more consistent energy stream. In California at the time, most companies supplied electricity only at night time, to illuminate people's homes. Richardson managed to convince the Ontario Electric Company to supply electricity to homes during the daytime on Tuesdays, the traditional day for ironing after the Monday weekly wash.

Despite Richardson's giant leap in innovation, electric irons remained hazardous. They would overheat or the cords would burn through. Newspapers at the time were riddled with reports of house fires started by electric irons. Safety organisations wrestled with the psychological shift required in the minds of consumers to coerce them into using electrical appliances more cautiously. In 1923 the *New York Times* interviewed a safety analyst called Dana Pierce. He is quoted as saying, 'Womankind has heretofore dealt with things that get cooler when left alone. The pot that has come off the stove, the old-fashioned iron – such things are safe enough when they're left by themselves ... And so they tend to use the electric iron as they have used all such things instinctively. But the hazard of the electric iron is that the heat piles up'. Finally, he warns, 'The housewife must not let it alone'. This made cordless models popular for a period as they were deemed safer, yet they remained insufficient as they cooled too quickly. The introduction of the automatic thermostat in the 1920s helped to regulate the heat in electric irons, making them much safer to use.

The arrival of steam irons further improved the ability of these devices to eradicate creases. The Steam-O-Matic was a particularly successful model. Made of aluminium, it weighed just 3 ½ pounds, a massive difference from the heavy sad irons of the Victorian period. However, in 1938 the Steam-O-Matic cost $9.95 (about $180 with inflation) making it an expensive home appliance, for use primarily by the middle and upper classes. Despite its cost, the Steam-O-Matic became a market leader. In a 1952 advertisement in *Life* magazine, the company proclaimed the 'most exciting discovery in ironing history ... you can now scent your lovely things as you iron'. A vial of scent could be poured into the steam funnel to add a fresh aroma to your laundry. In the long evolution of the iron this was hardly world changing but it symbolises the rich spirit of innovation associated with this deceptively simple household appliance.

THE CONDOM

'**B**ono and his band U2 ... will pay the Irish Family Planning Association's £500 fine for selling condoms in Dublin's Virgin Megastore,' reads an article in the *Evening Herald* in February 1991. Ironically, this legal case, which required Richard Branson to make an appearance in court for his shop's disobedience, marked the culmination of Ireland's long journey towards the acceptance of contraception.

Before the late 1970s it was illegal to import or sell condoms in the Republic of Ireland. In 1971 members of the Irish Women's Liberation Movement took the 'contraceptive train' to Belfast. They purchased condoms in the North and then arrived back in Connolly Station in Dublin with their contraband, in an audacious move to raise awareness of the country's anachronistic laws. A tradition of conservative values and the power of the Catholic Church meant that any liberation of the law in this area was extremely slow and often reluctant.

Charlie Haughey, the Fianna Fail Minister for Health at that time, introduced limited legislation in 1978. This required people to get a prescription from their doctor in order to purchase a condom. By 1985 condoms had become available in pharmacies without prescription. But access remained an issue as condoms couldn't be legally procured outside of business hours or from vending machines. 'The government were also under pressure from the other parties to review the family planning legislation, in order to increase the number of outlets selling condoms in an all-out effort to stop the spread of AIDS, or as the Fine Gael spokesperson for health, Richard Bruton, said, "face up to the realities of life in Ireland in the 1990s", writes Chrystel Hug in *The Politics of Sexual Morality in*

Ireland. The Virgin Megastore case caused an outcry and acted as a major catalyst for change. Slowly, restrictions on accessibility to condoms began to evaporate.

Elsewhere in the world, the existence and popular use of condoms goes back hundreds of years. In his memoirs, the eighteenth century adventurer and notorious lothario Giacomo Casanova describes trying on different sizes of condom. He writes, 'The girl came back with the packet and, putting myself in a proper position, I told her to try one on. She proceeded to do so with a sulky air and with a kind of repugnance which made me feel interested in her. Number one would not go on, so she had to try on a second, and the result was that I besprinkled her plentifully. The mistress laughed, but she was indignant, threw the whole packet in my face'.

This attests to the variance and untrustworthiness of pre-twentieth century condoms. They were objects in a process of constant trial and error. The word condom was already in use during Casanova's time. The etymology of the word is debated, but it may be derived from the Latin *condus*, meaning 'receptacle'. Others believe that the word comes from a Colonel Condum who prescribed sheaths to Charles II to prevent him from having so many illegitimate children. The French called the condom a *redingote anglaise* (English raincoat), while the English, in turn, described it as a 'French letter' (the idea being that anything sexual or hedonistic *must* be French in origin). The English also described it, in later times, as 'something for the weekend'.

Best known for giving his name to the fallopian tubes, the sixteenth century Italian anatomist and physician Gabriele Fallopio is often credited as the inventor of the modern condom. He developed a sheath designed to prevent the onset of venereal disease. It consisted of a linen cloth which was soaked in chemicals, wrapped around the penis and then tied at the base of the shaft with a ribbon. 'Falloppio recommended an ointment containing shavings of guaiacum and precipitated mercury, wine, flakes of copper, red coral, burnt ivory and burnt deer's horn,' says Caroline Rance in *The History of Medicine in 100 Facts*. 'When soaked in this mixture, the linen cover was ready for use and could be conveniently carried.' However, it is not clear whether his condom was actually used during sex or if it was applied *post coitus* as a way to kill any diseases picked up during intercourse. Fallopio tested his condom on over 1,000 men and proclaimed, 'I call immortal God to witness that not one of them was infected'.

The oldest condoms discovered by archaeologists were found in Dudley Castle in England. Dating from the 1640s, these are animal membrane sheaths and would have been used by soldiers loyal to Charles I during the English Civil War. It is likely that these condoms were intended to protect the user from sexually transmitted diseases such as syphilis, rather than to prevent impregnation.

Before the introduction of rubber in the 1850s, condoms were produced in slaughterhouses where animals' intestines and bladders were readily available to provide thin and elasticated membranes for use in prophylactics. These were then supplied to retail outlets. Writing in the *Atlantic*, historian Ruth Goodman says, 'The late eighteenth century saw the establishment of two shops in London devoted entirely to the sale of condoms. Made out of sheep guts, these condoms were carefully soaked for a couple of hours before use, to make them pliable and easy to put on. A ribbon was tied around the base to fasten them securely, and once they had been used, they were carefully washed out, allowed to dry, and stored in a small box until they were wanted again'.

Contraception has existed in one form or another since ancient times. A variety of extraordinary methods have been employed to stave off unwanted pregnancies. In Ancient Greece and Rome, one of the most common methods involved the use of silphium, a herb that was harvested into extinction, such was the demand. This was either drunk in water or made into a pessary. In another practice, which must have caused men's penises to sting terribly, Roman women would soak natural sea sponge in vinegar and insert it into the vagina prior to intercourse.

The Greek physician Soranus recommended the sneezing method. He explained, 'During the sexual act, at the critical moment of coitus when the man is about to discharge the seed, the woman must hold her breath and draw herself away a little, so that the seed may not be hurled too deep into the cavity of the uterus. And getting up immediately and squatting down, she should induce sneezing.' He also recommended the application of olive oil or honey to the vagina to help 'clog' the uterus. Hippocrates instructed women to drink copper ore, diluted in water. 'For a year, thereabouts, she does not get pregnant,' he promised rather hopefully.

The introduction of vulcanized rubber by Charles Goodyear in the mid-nineteenth century fundamentally changed the condom. 'On one occasion, the playwright George Bernard Shaw was supposed to have declared the rubber condom to be the greatest invention of the nineteenth century,' writes Robert Jütte in *Contraception: A History*. Although they were thick and uncomfortable, they were much cheaper than natural sheaths and by the 1850s they were gaining in popularity. 'In the late nineteenth century condom production began with a mold more or less in the shape of a penis, to which workers affixed strips of rubber, before it was then cured with heat,' according to Stephen L. Harp in his history of rubber. Rubber condoms came in a variety of sizes. However, they were often rather loose and some men chose to visit their doctor to get measured and then order a customised model. They generally lasted up to three months, requiring a simple rinse after each use.

One of the earliest advertisements for rubber condoms appeared in the *New York Times* in 1861. They were called Dr Power's French Preventatives and were manufactured by Goodyear. In 1870, the *Gentleman's Directory*, a naughty little guidebook for the men of New York City, advertised French Imported Male Safes, the word 'condom' still absent in advertising at this time. They were described as 'A perfect shield against disease or conception ... Made of both Skin and India Rubber'.

In 1919, an Ohio native by the name of Fred Killian invented the modern condom when he dipped a mould into latex. The first latex condom product, regretfully named 'Dreadnoughts,' went on the market in 1929. 'The resulting disposable latex condoms had a shelf life of about five years. The fact that they were thin, blocking sensation less than had earlier condoms, led to their widespread adoption in the United States,' argues Harp. In 1932, the London Rubber Company started manufacturing the first latex condoms for the European market. They called the product the Durex, derived from their principles of DUrability, Reliability and EXcellence. This would later become the company's official name and, indeed, one of the world's leading condom manufacturers.

▲ CONDOM MADE FROM ANIMAL GUT, LONDON, 1901-1930. SCIENCE MUSEUM, LONDON

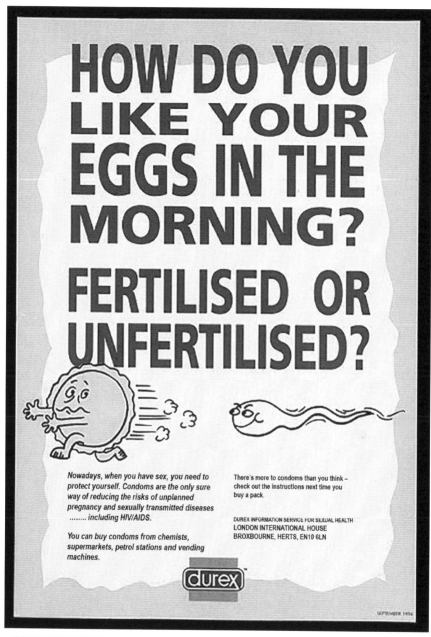

▲ DUREX ADVERTISEMENT, 1994. WELLCOME COLLECTION

TRAFFIC SIGNAL - FIFTH AVENUE AND 34TH STREET, 1922, NEW YORK

THE TRAFFIC LIGHT

John Peake Knight was working for the London, Brighton & South Coast Railway Company when he had the idea of adapting train traffic signals for regular roads. On December 9th, 1868, the world's first traffic light appeared at the junction of Great George Street and Bridge Street in Westminster, London. Cars didn't exist in the 1860s, of course, but horse carriages and pedestrian traffic warranted the introduction of a signalling system that would be more efficient than a lone policeman directing traffic in the middle of an intersection. According to 1866 statistics, over 1,000 people had died on London's roads and a further 1,300 had been injured, in that year alone.

Knight's new machine was operated manually by a policeman. 'For thirty seconds in every five minutes an arm of his proposed semaphore device would rise to horizontal and stop traffic and then lower to indicate traffic should proceed with caution,' according to James Winter in *London's Teeming Streets 1830-1914*. At night time the signals were given using gas powered red and green lights. The machine was 22-feet tall and made of cast iron in a typically ornate Victorian style, with acanthus leaf detailing and even topped with a pineapple finial.

A small article on the front page of local newspaper the *Tower Hamlets Independent* heralded the arrival of an invention which would eventually punctuate the corner of every street in every city of the world. It reported positively on the rather strange innovation, predicting the imminent spread of the technology across the metropolis: 'The diameter of the light is six inches, the signalling arms are four feet long, and the column, as a whole, presents a handsome appearance ... the general effect of the invention is the substitution of a gigantic signalling apparatus for a scarcely visible policeman'.

Knight's system came to an abrupt end in January 1870 when a steward who was operating the machine was maimed after a gas leak caused it to explode in his face. This unfortunate event, added to the perhaps precocious nature of the invention, stalled traffic light development until the early twentieth century.

The proliferation of cars in the second decade of the twentieth century created havoc on the streets. Horse carriages, pedestrians and motor cars all competed for space and gambled on the right of way at intersections. Cleveland, Ohio, played an important role in the development of a traffic light system which would solve some of these problems. The world's first electric traffic light launched in the city in 1914, on the junction of Euclid Avenue and 105th Street. It was designed by James Hoge and featured two coloured signals with the words 'Stop' and 'Move'. A buzzer sounded when the lights changed.

According to Megan Kate Nelson in the *Smithsonian Magazine*, 'A policeman sitting in a booth on the sidewalk could control the signals with a flip of a switch'. It was set up so that conflicting signals were impossible, thus avoiding collisions. Hoge's invention was considered so significant at the time that *The Motor*, the magazine of the Cleveland Automobile Club, said it was 'destined to revolutionize the handling of traffic in congested city streets and should be seriously considered by traffic committees for general adoption'.

In 1920, New York City announced a design competition for a series of 'traffic towers' to line Fifth Avenue. This was an attempt to control the ever increasing numbers of cars along the iconic thoroughfare. Architect Joseph Freedlander won the competition with his elegant 25-foot bronze towers, emblazoned with eagles and the crest of the city. A small glass cabin stood on top of the tower, in which a steward could operate the lights. Seven of the enormous towers were erected at intersections along the avenue, soaring over the traffic below, costing $125,000, a huge sum at the time. The *New York Times* reported that the lights were a success, reducing the journey time between 57th street and 43rd street from forty minutes to nine minutes.

However, by 1929 the towers were decommissioned to make way for newer technology. 'In 1931, Freedlander was back at it. He designed bronze traffic signals in a slimmed-down, *moderne* form of classicism that were topped by a Mercury-like figure, cast by the Tiffany studios,' says John Tauranac in

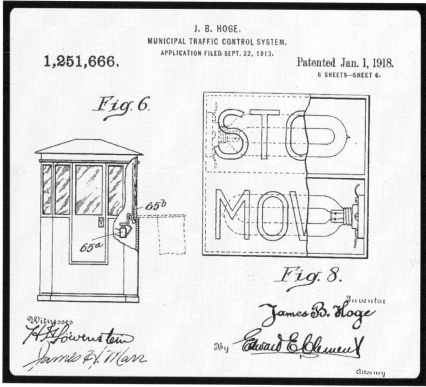

J. B. HOGE.

MUNICIPAL TRAFFIC CONTROL SYSTEM.

APPLICATION FILED SEPT. 22, 1913.

1,251,666.

Patented Jan. 1, 1918.

6 SHEETS—SHEET 6.

Fig. 6.

65*b*

65*a*

STO

MOV

Fig. 8.

Inventor

James B. Hoge

By Edward E. Clement

Attorney

Witnesses

▲ JAMES HOGE'S PATENT DESIGN FOR THE WORLD'S FIRST ELECTRONICALLY CONTROLLED TRAFFIC CONTROL SYSTEM

Manhattan's Little Secrets. 'Mercury was raising his right hand as if to say "Stop" … Those electric traffic signals were fully automated and they were placed on sidewalks at intersections, out of harm's way and visible to all.' Freedlander's lights continued in use until the mid-1960s.

In 1923, inventor Garrett Morgan introduced a very effective new measure, the warning signal. Prior to Morgan's idea, traffic signals switched from 'go' to 'stop', and vice versa, without any signal for the driver to *prepare* to go or stop. This led to accidents as stationary cars set off through lights, while other cars were still trying to get through from a previous signal. After witnessing a particularly horrible collision between a car and a horse-drawn carriage, Morgan determined to find a solution to this issue. His signal was T-shaped and had three positions: Go, Stop and All Stop, thereby creating a pause between converging traffic. It also gave time for pedestrians to cross safely. It was manually operated using a turning lever. At a similar time, a policeman name William Potts introduced a more effective warning system in Detroit. Potts' innovation was the amber light, which is of course still in use today.

The challenge for engineers was to create a traffic signal that was automatic and didn't require a steward to operate. The June 1928 edition of *Popular Science* elaborated on an early form of automation. Developed by Charles Adler, a railway signal engineer from Baltimore, his signal is amusing in retrospect, but was innovative at the time. The magazine explained, 'A cross street driver, wishing to pass, sounds his horn directly into an ordinary telephone transmitter. This device picks up the sound and operates an electric relay that changes the green light to red and the red light to green'. However, it didn't last long because his invention led to endless and tedious lines of honking cars, causing noise pollution for residents. Eventually, automatic lights operating on a time interval were installed in Wolverhampton in England during the same decade, changing the face of traffic management forever.

Ireland's first traffic lights were installed in August 1937, in Dublin. The *Irish Press* noted, 'Dubliners, ready at all times to stand and stare, had a regular field day yesterday when the new system of traffic lights, automatically controlled, came into operation at the junction of Merrion Street, Upper and Lower,

Clare Street and Merrion Square'. The newspaper went on to describe the presence of over a dozen Gardaí and tram workers on hand to help confused motorists navigate the new-fangled technology. However, one important international innovation in Ireland's first traffic light was the move away from 'timed intervals'. 'The lights are controlled by vehicular contact with rubber strands on the streets – a system that has been found to be superior to fixed time changing.'

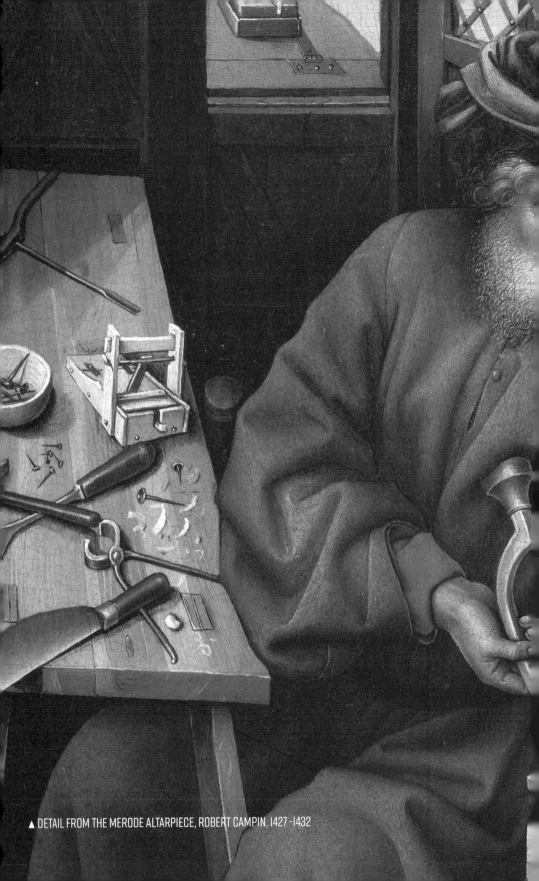

▲ DETAIL FROM THE MERODE ALTARPIECE, ROBERT CAMPIN, 1427-1432

10
THE mOUSE TRAP

In 1906, inventors Edward Markoff and Joseph Barad patented a mouse trap called a 'Device Employed for Exterminating Rats, Mice and Other Animals'. It consisted of a wooden box with a bait. The idea was that a mouse would enter an opening in the box, but in order to reach the bait it had to stretch its head through a noose. As the mouse lowered itself after successfully catching the cheese, the noose detached from the box and became a flexible collar around the animal's neck. The collar had a small bell attached to it. The terrified mouse would suddenly realise that no matter how it moved, it continued to make a frightful racket. The inventors hoped that it would then return to its family and petrify them into leaving the house altogether. As claimed in the patent, a bell's ringing is 'very terrifying to animals of the species named and that if pursued by such sounds they will immediately vacate their haunts and homes, never to return'.

Markoff and Barad's invention may seem hopeful at best, yet it is just one of over 4,400 mouse traps listed by the US Patent Office. To this day, over 20 new mouse trap ideas are considered each year, of which about a dozen get patented. The Patent Office even has different mouse trap categories, which include Impaling, Non-return Entrance, Choking or Squeezing, Constricting Noose and Electrocuting and Explosive. This makes it one of the most reinvented pieces of technology in history. The American philosopher Ralph Waldo Emerson is said to have proclaimed, 'Build a better mouse trap and the world will beat a path to your door'. Inventors have clearly been taking this advice very seriously. But why are we so zealous in our determination to rid our homes of mice?

The word 'mouse' comes from the Sanskrit *mus*, meaning 'thief'. The Romans adopted this word to describe both a mouse and a rat as *mus minimus* and *mus maximus*, which to me sound like brilliant names for cartoon characters. In his 1996 chronicle of mouse trap history for *American Heritage* magazine, Jack Hope estimates that in one year a single mouse can 'eat up four pounds of pantry food, deposit thirty-six thousand droppings, tear up a quilt or two for nesting material, and, in ten to twelve matings, beget itself ninety-nine times'. The *New York Times* puts it another way: 'One pair of mice can multiply into a family of two million in two years'. Despite their relatively harmless nature, people see mice as nasty multiplying thieves, trying to rob our kitchens and lackadaisically defecating all over our homes. Many people suffer from murophobia and simply can't bear the idea of sharing a house with our furry little friends. This has led to a long history of trying to exterminate them.

▲ NINETEENTH CENTURY ENGRAVING OF A MOUSE TRAP

In the Merode Altarpiece, Robert Campin's fifteenth century triptych, Joseph, the husband of Mary, is seen working in his carpentry studio. On his workbench is a mouse trap. It is no surprise that Joseph is depicted in this way as Saint Augustine was said to have used the symbol of the mouse trap to explain the purpose of Jesus' death. Art historian Meyer Schapiro writes, 'The cross of the Lord was the Devil's mouse trap (*muscipula diablo*); the bait by which he was caught was the

Lord's death'. The painting also offers us an insight into what mouse traps were like during the Renaissance. This particular one became known as the Merode mouse trap because of the painting's fame and it remained a popular device right up until the eighteenth century. It was a remarkably effective contraption which used a trigger and a torsion sprung rope to capture its victims. Once the rodent stepped on the trigger, lured by a bait, the spring released a slab of wood onto the mouse, killing it instantly.

According to Hope, before the nineteenth century, mouse traps were made by blacksmiths and craftsmen. 'These early, unpatented traps typically captured or killed mice by dropping them through hinged doors into containers of water.' These were called 'drowners'. But when the US Patent Office was established in 1838, craftsmen began to realise that they could make money from these devices and they slowly became objects of profit. By the late nineteenth century there was an explosion in mouse trap patents, with every imaginable idea being put forward as a solution to home infestation, from grisly guillotine traps to deadfalls.

One of the major issues which inventors wrestled with was how to get rid of the mangled corpse without creating a macabre mess. American Emmanuel T. Lynch, of Iowa, patented the first 'pierce and release' model in the late nineteenth century. This was a six-inch mahogany box containing a complex mechanism of springs and levers which, when triggered, punctured a rodent's shoulders in six places. The idea was that it terminally injured the mouse before it struggled free and died elsewhere, thereby saving the user from having to deal with the bloody corpse.

In typical Victorian fashion, many inventors turned to whimsy and developed traps which not only captured mice, but also entertained households at the same time. 'These "toy traps" typically lured a lone mouse onto or into a miniature moving mechanism that then began to turn, roll, or spin, propelled by the frightened creature's attempts to escape, presumably delighting all onlookers,' says Hope. They were similar to the spinning wheels that guinea pigs often play on, the difference being that this one entrapped an unwitting animal, with little chance of escape. Musical mouse traps also had their moment. An article in the *Irish Times* in 1897 reported that because 'mice are very sensitive to music, a Belgian manufacturer has substituted a musical mouse trap for the common trap ... The mice, he insists, are drawn irresistibly towards the music box, and in order to hear better they step into the trap and find themselves prisoners'.

The Perpetual mouse trap was one of the earliest 'humane' traps, designed to capture but not kill rodents. It was designed by Colin Pullinger in West Sussex in 1860. It came to public attention in 2016 when one particular antique trap came back to life in an extraordinary moment reminiscent of the *Night at the Museum* franchise. In February of that year, staff at the Museum of English Rural Life in Reading were startled to discover that their Perpetual had come out of retirement to capture a mouse, which had sneaked into the museum, over 150 years after the trap was made. According to the museum, 'it is a multi-catch trap with a see-saw mechanism'. This allows a mouse into the wooden box but they are unable to get out again, thereby trapping the rodent. The Perpetual was a commercial success and Pullinger's company would go on to sell over a million mouse traps across Britain.

There continued to be a demand for humane mouse traps during the twentieth century. The American market was decades behind the UK in live trap technology, with their first successful model emerging as late as 1930. Austin Kness was working as a caretaker in a school in Iowa when he noticed mice getting into the children's lunchboxes. He set about fashioning a trap which could contain live mice without harming them. He christened it the Ketch-All. It was a metal box with an entrance that acted like a revolving door which the mouse could enter but couldn't exit. Remarkably, the machine didn't use any bait, unlike Pullinger's Perpetual trap, but instead depended on the 'curiosity' of the mouse. When the animal stepped on a weight-sensitive pad it triggered a mechanism that 'spanked' the mouse inside, where it was held in a special chamber with the other unfortunate prisoners. It could contain 15 mice at a time before it needed to be emptied. The paddle which pushed the mouse inside the chamber was powered by a wind-up key that the user set before use.

Trapping expert Shawn Woods has a fascinating archive of vintage mouse traps on his website Mousetrap Monday. He warns that, although the Ketch-All is designed to keep the mice alive, it can occasionally have some unintended consequences. 'Sometimes with these live animal traps, when you condense a bunch of animals in a small space, I've seen them kill and eat each other. They turn into cannibals.' This unfortunate possibility aside, Kness's design spawned many imitators in the American market, but his original company is still producing the Ketch-All to this day.

James Henry Atkinson, an English ironmonger, patented perhaps the world's most successful mouse trap, the Little Nipper, in 1898. Patented as 'An Improved treadle trap for mice, rats and the like', the Little Nipper is a small wooden snap trap which is now so recognisable that it is the most likely image

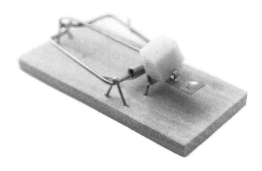

▲ LITTLE NIPPER MOUSE TRAP

conjured in the mind when we think of mouse traps. It consists of a treadle which a mouse steps on to retrieve the bait. This sets off a spring, releasing a kill bar which snaps the neck of the mouse. The kill bar lands at 38/1000ths of a second, making it one of the fastest and most efficient traps ever invented. Atkinson sold his patent to a company called Procter for £1,000. It is still manufactured and dominates about 60% of the British market to this day.

In 1980, the mouse trap industry moved in a rather sinister direction with a number of manufacturers producing glue traps for the first time. These were shallow trays with a special adhesive that mice simply couldn't escape from and would eventually cause them to die of exhaustion. 'Many mice and other small animals caught by glue traps end up gnawing off limbs or tearing skin in an attempt to escape. They've also been known to suffocate after getting their faces stuck to the cardboard or plastic that makes up the bulk of the trap,' reports Nicholas Jackson in *The Atlantic*.

Sales for these new traps skyrocketed during the '80s. Jack Hope describes them as 'demonic' and perhaps the cruellest form of entrapment created in the long history of mouse traps. He writes, 'It was only after consumers began to realize that whenever they followed their glue trap's instructions to throw out trap and mouse together, they were, often as not, depositing a still-living, still-struggling, and still-shrieking mouse in the garbage, that sales began to level off'. Glue traps were so abhorrent to some people that the government in the state of Victoria, in Australia, banned them in 2008. But one thing is sure – as long as mice continue to invade our homes, the market for mouse traps will continue to prosper, in one form or another.

ODO-RO-NO saves Dresses
Guards DAINTINESS

GET THE SURE PROTECTION ODO-RO-NO GIVES!

EVEN the best of dry cleaning can't remove the perspiration stains that fade and taint good dresses. And a girl loses her attractiveness to friends the minute underarm odour can be noticed.

Underarm moisture must be prevented — and Odorono is your one dependable protection. It's a doctor's own prescription that safely and surely does prevent this needless perspiration. Odorono saves money in clothing bills. It insures your freshness.

Odorono is the famous, original perspiration preventive. Odorono Regular (ruby-red) gives the longest protection of any product of its kind. You use it just once or twice a week. The new type— quick-drying Instant Odorono (colourless) is formulated for women who prefer to use Odorono every day.

So Convenient

BOTH TYPES HAVE THE ORIGINAL ODORONO HYGIENIC APPLICATOR

Enclosed is 4d. in stamps for samples of Instant Odorono, Odorono Regular & Deodorant Crème Odorono.

NORTHAM WARREN, Ltd. (Dept. F.43), 215, Blackfriars Road, LONDON, S.E.1

Name........................

Address........................

ODO·RO·NO

11
DEODORANT

In 1919, a start-up deodorant company called Odorono (Odour? Oh no!), based in Cincinnati, took out a full-page advertisement in the *Ladies Home Journal*. The banner headline read, 'Within the Curve of a Woman's Arm: A frank discussion of a subject too often avoided'. The copy went on to suggest that a woman's arm 'should be the daintiest, prettiest thing in the world. And yet, unfortunately, it isn't always'. The advertising executive hired by the company was tasked with finding a way to convince women that they needed a product that nobody was buying and which was exceptionally taboo at that time. Discussion of women's intimate hygiene needs was so controversial that many women immediately cancelled their subscriptions to the magazine.

Despite these obstacles, the advertising firm realised that the best way to sell their product was to persuade women that body odour was socially unacceptable because it threatened women's 'daintiness' (see opposite) and would jeopardise their prospects of marriage. Another ad from the same company reads, 'The most humiliating moment in my life: when I overheard the cause of my unpopularity among men'. Within a year of the original advert, sales had increased by 112%.

We have tried to deodorise ourselves for thousands of years, in a desperate bid to mask the fetid stench of our bodies. Sweat in itself is not offensive, but when it interacts with the bacteria on our skin it creates body odour. There are two types of deodorant: ordinary deodorant and antiperspirant deodorant. Ordinary deodorant kills the bacteria on our skin. However, it doesn't reduce the amount of sweat we produce. Antiperspirant stops the creation of sweat by plugging our sweat glands with special salts.

For much of history we used perfumes to hide bad odour. The Ancient

Egyptians would put scented waxes in their hair which would melt in the sun, delivering a pleasant aroma. In the ninth century a man named Abu Ziryab played a profound role in the development of a culture of personal hygiene. He lived in the city of Cordoba (now in modern-day Spain) which was a major Islamic centre in the Middle Ages. A musician who was interested in cosmetics, he believed in the treatment of perspiration and regular bathing and changing of clothes. A Medieval metrosexual, so to speak. He concocted one of the world's first ever deodorants. It contained protoxyde of lead to combat body odour and he recommended that courtiers in Cordoba apply his solution regularly.

Modern deodorant, as we know it today, began to develop only in the late nineteenth century. The first commercial deodorant was called Mum, patented in Philadelphia in 1888, a company still producing deodorants today. It was a zinc based cream which was said to kill the bacteria on the skin. But early deodorants were very niche products. If people were especially concerned with sweat, they would wear underarm cotton or rubber pads or simply change their shirts more regularly than usual.

Odorono changed all this with their bold advertising campaign and is often considered the progenitor of the modern deodorant industry. But how did it come about?

In 1909, Dr Abraham Murphey set about creating a product which could help surgeons with excessively sweaty hands. He created an antiperspirant solution containing aluminium chloride that could be rubbed on the hands to block the pores of the skin. Dr Murphey's daughter saw a wider potential for the product and set about adapting it as a woman's personal 'toilet water'. Her eventual product came as a liquid in an elegant glass bottle.

Odorono came with detailed instructions on how to use it correctly. This was especially important as the acidity of the product could inflame the skin. The company recommended that women refrained from shaving their underarms before application in order to avoid sensitivity. The liquid was red in colour so users had to be careful that the product didn't stain their clothes. Unlike modern consumer habits of applying antiperspirant in the mornings, Odorono was a bedtime ablution. Advertisements advised that 'the right time to use Odorono is at night before retiring. Pat it on the underarms with a bit of absorbent cotton, only two or three times a week. Then a little talcum dusted on and you can forget all about that worst of all embarrassments'. This type of advertising

Perspiration odour ruins romance !

Trouble in the air . . .

Don't wait till this happens to you! Make sure you are nice to be near with Mum Cream. Clinical tests by skin specialists have proved that Mum actually stops perspiration odour 24 hours a day. Yet gentle Mum does not interfere with natural perspiration.
Buy Mum Cream — and use it always !

Standard size **2/-** *New Handy size* **10d.**

Effective
MUM Cream
stops perspiration odour best!

Product of Bristol-Myers Co. Limited, London & New York

▲ ORIGINAL MAGAZINE ADVERTISEMENT FOR MUM PERSPIRATION CREAM, 1950S was alarmingly forthright when it was published in 1919. The copywriter, James Young, later said, 'Several women who learned that I had written this advertisement said they would never speak to me again - that it was "disgusting" and "an insult to women"'.

It wasn't until the 1940s that an antiperspirant was developed with lower acidity levels. Skin irritation didn't help advertisers who were also trying to fight another battle: the claim by many doctors that antiperspirant was bad for your health. It was argued that the blocking of the pores was unhealthy for the body. Like so many consumer products of the early to mid-twentieth century, other doctors were brought on board by advertisers to dismiss such claims and reassure customers that the product was safe to use.

Most early deodorants were squarely aimed at women. One attempt to capture the male market can be seen in a 1917 Odorono advert which appealed to golfers. 'Perspiring hands have lost many a match,' reads the copy, advising gentlemen golfers to apply the product an hour before teeing off for a sweatless round. But there is no mention of applying the product to the underarms. A pungent musk was considered manly until deodorant companies realised that they could double their market if they started targeting men too.

Men's deodorants were advertised differently to the women's market. 'In 1935, Top-Flite, the first deodorant targeted at men, hit store shelves in its sleek black bottle, followed by other stereotypically male designs, like the Seaforth bottle resembling a miniature whiskey jug,' according to social historian Hunter Oatman-Stanford. 'Advertisements for men's deodorant products often focused on financial insecurities, positing that foul body odors might ruin one's career.' A 1941 advertisement for Mum features an office worker called Jim who doesn't get a pay rise until he starts using deodorant. 'The difference between $35 a week and higher brackets may very well be Mum,' reads the ad.

Deodorant, as a consumer product, played a significant role in the evolution of shame-based advertising, a cornerstone of the ways in which companies convince consumers to buy their products. Historian Cari Casteel writes, 'Many early deodorant advertisements actively shamed consumers into purchasing their product. Men and women were told that if they did not wear a deodorant it would lead to other failures: in love, friendship, and business'.

In 1952, Mum, the original inventor of modern commercial deodorant, launched the world's first roll-on product. They adopted the technology used in the ballpoint pen, which had been conceived just fourteen years earlier. Finally, Gillette designed the first spray deodorant in the late 1960s and named it Right Guard. Its slogan was 'Nothing touches you but the spray itself'.

JIM'S SALARY CHECKS HAVE traced a sharp upward curve—since he began with Mum. Energy and experience, brains and personality being nearly equal—the difference between $35 a week and higher brackets may very well be Mum!

▲ 1940S ADVERTISEMENT FOR MUM

▲ HUBERT CECIL BOOTH'S ORIGINAL VACUUM CLEANER, SUPPLIED TO THE ROYAL NAVAL COLLEGE, ISLE OF WIGHT, C.1905. SCIENCE MUSEUM, LONDON

THE VACUUM CLEANER

The Vacuum Cleaner Company, of Victoria Street in London, posted a newspaper advertisement in 1906. It read, 'Carpets, Curtains, Upholstered Furniture and Bedding cleaned, renovated and thoroughly freed of dust, without removal from the house, or any disturbance to the inmates … This process is speedy, inexpensive and healthy'. This new service was patented by English engineer Hubert Cecil Booth in 1901, the year of Queen Victoria's death. It was a revolution in home cleaning. Booth's Puffing Billy, a gasoline piston machine, was so large that it had to be carried on a horse drawn carriage. Long hoses were then fed from the parked carriage out on the road, in through the windows of a building, to perform the device's vacuuming miracle. It took four people to operate it.

'Before long, he was asked to perform unusual jobs,' writes Gilly Pickup in *What the British Invented*. 'One was to clean the girders of the Crystal Palace, which were thick with layers of dust accumulated over the years. He didn't send only one machine to do the job as he was asked; he sent fifteen of them.' By the end of the job, Booth's machines had vacuumed 26 tonnes of dust. Clearly not a place for those suffering with hay fever. The sudden arrival of the vacuum cleaner must have given rise to an alarming realisation of the enormous amount of dust in our lives. Soon, wealthy homeowners were hiring Cecil Booth's services to clean their own carpets. The technology was so novel that parties were organised around the event, with guests marvelling at the uniformed vacuumers carrying out their extraordinary work. The Puffing Billy was even used to clean the carpets of Westminster Abbey in preparation for the coronation of Edward VII in 1902.

The carpet sweeper was the dominant device in use before the development of motorised cleaners in the late nineteenth century. In 1876 a Michigan couple, Melville and Ana Bissell, produced perhaps the most famous carpet sweeper of the period. The 'Grand Rapids', named after their hometown, consisted of a small wooden box on wheels, with a long handle for the user to control. A cylindrical rotating brush was attached to the wheels. As the device was pushed across a carpet, the wheels turned the brush, kicking up dirt into the box. The Bissell's carpet sweeper remained popular right into the twentieth century and is still made today.

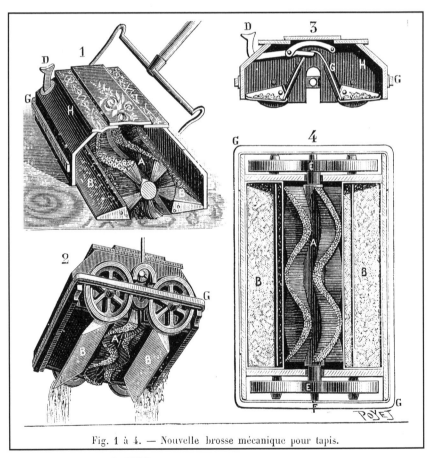

Fig. 1 à 4. — Nouvelle brosse mécanique pour tapis.

▲ DIAGRAM OF A CARPET SWEEPER

Early advertisements for the Bissell had to persuade consumers to move away from the centuries-old tradition of using a broom, towards an entirely new approach. One ad asked readers 'Why waste your energies sweeping with a corn broom (a sweeping brush made with corn husks), when at a small cost you can procure a BISSELL sweeper? No woman prefers a corn broom to a carpet sweeper, but under the mistaken idea that it's more economical she keeps sweeping in the old, laborious, back-breaking way'.

In 1899, American John Thurman patented his 'pneumatic carpet renovator', a machine which operated on the opposite principle to what Booth would create just two years later. Powered by petrol, Thurman's machine delivered a blast of air which kicked dirt and debris up into a receptacle. Home visits cost $4 (about $116 in today's money). Despite his best efforts, Thurman's invention simply wasn't effective enough. It operated much like a leaf blower does today and it was, therefore, extremely difficult to control the agitated dust and successfully collect it in the canvas receptacle.

Thurman exhibited his invention at the Empire Music Hall in London in 1901. Hubert Cecil Booth happened to be at the event and engaged in a now infamous exchange with Thurman about the shortcomings of his device. Booth recalled the event much later in his 1936 *The Origins of the Vacuum Cleaner*: 'I asked the inventor why he did not suck out the dust ... The inventor became heated, remarking that sucking out dust was impossible, as it had been tried over and over without success: he then walked away'.

Booth became fascinated with the potential of suction. He later recounted a story about his moment of epiphany. He attached a white handkerchief to the back of a plush chair in a London restaurant. He then applied his mouth to the handkerchief and sucked as hard as he could muster. When he examined his hankie he noticed that it was black with dust. From there he set about creating a machine which could accomplish the same result, but on a larger scale. He used a five-horsepower motor to rotate a fan. The fan created a small vacuum at its rear which drew air inwards. He then attached a tube to the machine which could pull debris into the space created by the vacuum. This was the operating principle behind the Puffing Billy, his first commercial vacuuming enterprise.

Despite the success of the Puffing Billy, there was a demand for a smaller, portable machine which could work just as well as Cecil Booth's giant apparatus. James Spangler, a janitor in an Ohio department store, used a Bissell carpet sweeper during his shift each evening. He suffered from asthma and the Bissell had a tendency to throw excess dust into the air, agitating Spangler's breathing. Drawing inspiration form the mechanics of a street cleaning machine, he set about devising the world's first successful portable vacuum cleaner. 'It consisted of an electric fan motor driving home-made fan blades housed in a soap box with a cylindrical sweeping brush at the front and a pillowcase as a dust collector, all pushed along by a broom handle,' according to Robin Roy in his book on product innovation.

Spangler set up the Electric Sweeper Suction Company and refined his machine over time using better equipment and materials. His cousin Susan was impressed with his invention and persuaded her husband William Hoover, a leather goods manufacturer, to invest in the company. Hoover had been looking for ways to diversify his business and bought Spangler's patents in 1908. He retained the inventor as a superintendent in the business.

'The manufacture of electric cleaners was at first a side line in the W.H. Hoover Company,' according to Carroll Gantz in *The Vacuum Cleaner: A History*. 'A room in the leather goods factory was set aside for a small force of 20 people ... In August 1908 the Hoover Model O went into production, coloured black.' It was a heavy (18kg) and cumbersome machine by modern standards, with a large bag attached to the handle for collecting debris. It cost $60 (about $1,600 in today's money) and was very much the preserve of wealthy households, considering the average wage was a dollar a day for regular working men at that time. The *Saturday Evening Post* ran an advertisement for the Model O in 1909. It was described as a Hoover Electric Suction Sweeper and instructed users on how it operated. 'It works like magic. Simply attach the wire to an electric light socket, turn on the current and run the machine over the carpet as you would an ordinary carpet sweeper.'

Soon competition grew as more and more manufacturers started producing portable vacuum cleaners for the home. Unlike today, early advertising often focused on the machines' ability to clean not just carpets, but to remove dust from furniture, hats and even clothes. Many companies stressed the hygienic benefits of purchasing their machine, argues Gantz. In 1909, an advertisement for the Ideal vacuum stated: 'It eats up the dirt: literally sucks out all the dust, grit, germs, moths and eggs of vermin that are on the object as well as in it – gobbles them down into its capacious maw, never to trouble you again'. The age of endless vacuuming had well and truly begun, as the Hoover brand quickly became synonymous with vacuuming around the world.

▲ AMERICAN VACUUM CLEANER ADVERT, 1908

▲ CUTTLERY SET, MID EIGHTEENTH CENTURY.
© VICTORIA AND ALBERT MUSEUM, LONDON
COURTESY OF THE ROSALINDE AND ARTHUR GILBERT COLLECTION

THE FORK

The story of the fork is closely aligned with what sociologists call the 'civilising process'. This simple table instrument reflects the social constructs of what people feel is the mannerly or 'proper' way to behave during meals. The sociologist Norbert Elias argues that the use of the fork filtered down through the class system, operating as an instrument of the civilising process and making it less and less socially acceptable to use your fingers to eat food. The middle classes wished to emulate their superiors and, therefore, adopted the fork too, and so on until its use became more and more widespread.

It is also the story of how women, spaghetti and ruffle cuffs made the fork what it is today. The knife and the spoon were in existence long before the fork. Both are essential for cutting meat and lifting liquid. But the fork, in many ways, is an accessory rather than an essential. In fact, the evolution of the fork is perhaps more cultural than functional.

A long two-pronged fork had been in use in Ancient Greece and Rome for lifting meat out of large cauldrons. The idea of transferring this technology to the dinner table hadn't caught on yet. Before the arrival of the table fork, people largely ate with their hands and a knife, making meals a rather sticky affair. This continued right up to the Medieval period, and indeed longer in some parts of Europe. Table knives were often pointed so users could spear their food and lift it to their mouths.

We know that the fork was being used at dinner tables in the Byzantine empire by the eleventh century. In 1004, a princess named Maria Argyropoulina married the son of the Doge of Venice. She exerted her Byzantine influence when she brought her personal set of gold eating forks with her to the Venetian court. When she used them at the banquet after the wedding ceremony it caused an outrage. One local priest wrote, 'God in his wisdom has provided man with natural forks – his fingers. Therefore, it is an insult to him to substitute artificial metal forks for them when eating'. When Maria died from plague just a few years after her marriage, many considered it a justified divine punishment.

Many people in Europe continued to eat their food out of 'trenchers' – plate shaped chunks of stale bread which could be brought directly to the mouth to slurp the contents. The trencher itself was either devoured at the end of the meal or thrown to the dogs under the table. What a brilliant way to save on the washing up.

It seems baffling to us now that the fork didn't catch on more quickly. Yet the fork continued to be an object of both fear and derision in Europe. Some have speculated that this was due to its resemblance to the devil's pitchfork, itself borrowed from the instrument wielded by the Greek god Poseidon. In fact, the Latin word for fork, *furca*, has its basis in this meaning. The fork became a source of terror in Christian iconography. One of the earliest representations of this is Muiredach's High Cross in Monasterboice, Co. Louth, dating from the tenth

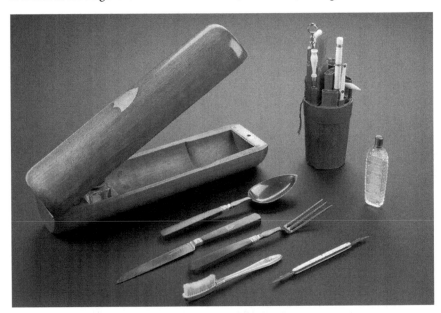

▲ NAPOLEONIC CUTLERY AND TOILET CASE. SCIENCE MUSEUM, LONDON

century. On the right-hand side, we can see the devil herding the souls away from Jesus using a three-pronged pitchfork. If anything was going to discourage diners from using a fork with their meal, then surely this was.

The rise in the consumption of pasta in Italy played a crucial role in the adoption of the fork in ever widening circles. Spaghetti in particular was too awkward to eat without a fork, which was easily able to twirl the strands onto itself. Gentlemen in Renaissance Italy would carry a *cadena* with them when they visited other people's homes. A *cadena* was an ornate wooden box which held your personal fork and spoon. The Victoria and Albert Museum has a number of personal cutlery cases in its collection. 'Up to the eighteenth century it was customary to have a personal set of cutlery, which people would take wherever they went to eat,' according to the museum. From the seventeenth century, the fork was added to these gilt leather cases. It wasn't the custom for women to carry knives, so the men were obliged to cut women's meat for them. This required a lot of stretching across tables and the general treatment of women like members of a children's tea party. After the meal it was acceptable for diners to simply wipe their hands on the table cloth.

Small fruit forks had been used in France since the reign of Charles V in the fourteenth century. However, these were only used for eating fruits such as mulberries or blackberries to prevent staining the fingers. The notion of using a larger Italian-style fork during a savoury meal was introduced by a French teenager. In 1533 Catherine de Medici, at the age of just 14, was packed off to France to marry the future King Henry II. She brought the Florentine fork to the French court and its use began to spread. The precocious princess also brought her own personal confectioners and distillers with her. Sweets and booze. People started drinking much younger in the sixteenth century.

The fork eventually arrived in England in the seventeenth century. The travel writer Thomas Coryate, who is mentioned in the chapter on the umbrella, brought a fork back to England after a trip to Italy. Forks of this period in Italy would have been made from iron, steel or silver and Coryate had been astonished by their popularity. In his 1608 book *Coryate's Crudities* he wrote, 'The Italian, and also most strangers that are commorant in Italy, doe alwaies, at their meales use a little forke when they cut the meate ... so that whatsoever he be that sitteth in the company of any others ... should unadvisedly touch the dish of meate with his fingers, from which all at the table doe cut, he will give occasion of offence unto the company as having transgressed the lawes of good manners'.

Coryate was attempting to explain something very foreign to a suspicious audience. Historian Anna Suryani goes further and says, 'Coryate, who demonstrated his exceptional open mindedness more than once in his narrative, suggested in this instance that it was the English who were less civilized'. Coryate claimed to be the first person in London to own a fork and he got the nickname *furciferus* (pitchfork handler) as a result. He was mercilessly mocked for his fork use, with his friend Ben Jonson writing that they were 'Brought into custom here, as they are in Italy, To the sparing of napkins'.

Bee Wilson discusses the complex gender identities associated with the fork in her book *Consider the Fork: A History of How We Cook and Eat*. She says that 'as late as 1897 British sailors were still demonstrating their manliness by eating without forks'. The English saw the fork as an affectation, something effeminate that real men didn't require. However, with the rising men's fashion of long ruffle lace cuffs (the opposite of effeminate, of course), the fork soon became necessary if you didn't want to get your sleeves covered in juicy boiled calf's head, a typical fork friendly dish of the time. 'Even Puritans used them,' says Wilson. 'In 1659, Richard Cromwell, son of Oliver Cromwell and the second Lord Protector, paid £2 8s for six meat forks.'

▲ LATE SEVENTEENTH CENTURY THREE-TINED ITALIAN FORK. THE ROBERT L. METZENBERG COLLECTION

We must not forget the usefulness of this trusty mainstay of the cutlery drawer. Although its evolution is intricately tied to the civilising process, it was also an instrument which made eating easier. The two tines, or prongs, of an eighteenth century fork could hold a piece of meat firmly in place, without swiveling around the plate as you cut it with a knife. The fork became ever more useful after a third and, eventually, a fourth tine were added in Germany. With the addition of extra tines also came a deeper curve in the fork, allowing users to not only hold meat while cutting it, but also to scoop up food from a plate too.

The fork had well and truly established itself not just as a useful accompaniment to the knife, but also as a symbol of one's civilised status.

Swanson Night... everybody wins!

Each one can pick his favorite meal (like this golden shrimp) and join in the after-dinner fun.

"Gee, this sauce makes the shrimp extra-good."

LOOK

Swanson gives you tangy cocktail sauce as an extra "home style" touch!

SWANSON FROZEN FRIED SHRIMP DINNER

- Swanson Shrimp—fried crispy on the outside, *juicy* and tender on the inside.
- Young green peas in seasoned butter sauce.
- "Crinkle-cut" potatoes for more crispness. Carefully fried to keep them light and tender.
- The perfect complement for fried shrimp —a tart, tangy, tomato cocktail sauce.

Have a Swanson Night soon!

Trust Swanso

"TV" and "TV Dinner" are registered trademarks of Campbell Soup Compa

▲ SWANSON TV DINNER ADVERTISEMENT, 1963

THE READY MEAL

In 1979, Cathy Chapman, a product developer with Marks & Spencer, had a radical idea. She suggested selling a chicken Kiev ready meal to their customers. Frozen and dehydrated pre-cooked dinners already existed, but Chapman wanted to create a fresh ready meal for a more discerning customer. A few weeks before the launch of her new product, a major point of contention arose with the Marks & Spencer board ... was the British public ready for garlic?

Garlic was an exotic flavour in the 1970s and was perceived as being too risky for the national palette. Ever since the seventeenth century the British had been suspicious of garlic. In John Evelyn's 1699 compendium on salads, he forbade their inclusion in any recipes due to their 'intolerable rankness'. He continued, 'to be sure, tis' not for Ladies pallats, nor those who court them'.

Despite her superiors' initial scepticism, Chapman's chicken Kiev was launched, with garlic intact, to great acclaim. It cost £1.99, which was very expensive (about £10 in today's money), yet middle and higher income earners flocked to buy it. Chilli con carne and chicken tikka masala soon followed suit.

Although Chapman had succeeded in gentrifying the ready meal, the history of pre-prepared cooking goes back to the great advances in food preservation in early twentieth century America.

The story of ready-made meals begins with the quick-freezing process developed and mastered by Clarence Birdseye during the 1920s. Birdseye, the father of frozen food, changed the way people eat. Mechanical cooling systems had been developed during the 1870s, allowing the freezing of meat and fish. This system replaced the inefficient ice box prevalent at the time. But freezing remained an imperfect art. It was a slow process which allowed large ice crystals to form. Thawing created wet, poorly textured meat. 'Many people believed that

▲ 1941 BIRDS EYE FROSTED FOODS ADVERT

frozen foods were unhealthful; others did not like the taste or smell of thawed food ... Some companies froze inferior quality food, knowing that it would be impossible for consumers to tell the difference between good and bad food at the point of sale, writes Andrew F. Smith in *Eating History*.

Birdseye had an epiphany while working as a fur trader in Labrador, in Canada. In order to preserve meat, the Inuits would dip it in the water and then the Arctic wind would very quickly freeze it. He was astonished that even several months after freezing, the meat retained its quality. The fast-freezing process created very small ice crystals in the meat which didn't damage the tissue structure. In the mid-1920s he established his own company and invented the Multiplate Quick Frozen Machine to emulate the ideas of his northern friends.

Birdseye was a pioneer in a world that wasn't quite ready for him. At first, shops simply didn't have the freezer equipment to store his seafood products. The restaurant and hotel trade were used to dealing with large frozen sides of beef, but it was virtually unheard of to purchase small family-sized frozen foods in grocery shops. A company called General Foods understood his vision and bought all of his 168 patents for a total of $22 million dollars and trademarked the Birdseye brand, just before the Wall Street Crash in 1929. Food historian Judith Jango-Cohen says, 'Birdseye "Frosted Foods" first went on sale in the United States on March 6th, 1930. Advertisements told customers, "You can buy them ready to cook or eat! No work on your part. You will see meat, fish, oysters ... even June peas and rich, red raspberries"'. Slowly more and more shops began to invest in freezer compartments, so that by the early 1940s the company was thriving. Birdseye's mastering of the quick-freezing process paved the way for the introduction of the ready meal. Convenience food had arrived.

The airline industry was an early adopter of ready meals. Prior to the 1940s the culinary experience in the skies was very different to the post-war period. In 1939 Pan Am started serving freshly cooked meals onboard their Boeing 314 Clipper. This aircraft was used for their first transatlantic service, which flew from Long Island to Marseille, via the Azores. The journey took 24 hours and a return ticket cost $675 (about $11,000 in today's money). For that price, the passengers expected some decent grub. They weren't disappointed. Full roast dinners were prepared on board and everything was cooked in traditional electric ovens in the galley. These veritable feasts took up to two hours to cook. A special area of

▲ LUNCH ON THE PLANE, PAN AM, 1977

the aircraft was set up with a table with linen cloths and silver cutlery. 'Since there was only room for twelve people at the table and the aircraft held more than that, passengers dined in shifts,' according to Richard Foss in *Food in the Air and Space*.

This meal system changed when the Naval Air Transportation Service introduced ready meals for their transatlantic flights, during World War Two. These were developed by New York inventor William Maxson. 'Called Strato-Plates, these first frozen in-flight meals offered a portion of meat – ham, breaded veal cutlets, or beef stew – and two vegetables,' says Smith. The food was arranged on compartmentalised paper plates, quick-frozen and then later heated in a special convection oven that Maxson designed to be light enough for use in an aircraft. It was able to heat six trays of food in 15 minutes, many times faster than regular ovens at that time. After the war, Pan Am began using Maxson's system. This technology transformed airplane food and ready meals became standard in the skies from the 1950s onwards.

Gerry Thomas, a salesman with a Nebraskan frozen food company called C.A. Swanson & Sons, adapted the airplane ready meal for general consumption in the mid-1950s. The company had found itself with a surplus of turkey meat after Thanksgiving one year and Thomas suggested the idea of preparing the meat as a ready-cooked frozen meal. This business model had become viable with the proliferation of fridges with freezer compartments in post-war America. 'First sold in 1954, just as television was becoming the dominant family pastime, the Swanson TV Dinner was packaged in a box designed to look like a TV screen … it consisted of turkey, cornbread dressing and gravy, buttered peas and sweet potatoes,' reported the *New York Times*.

Thomas's idea had such a revolutionary impact on the way people consumed food that the Smithsonian National Museum of American History retains an original aluminium Swanson TV dinner tray in its collection to this day. 'It offered women – more and more of whom were working outside the home, but still assumed to be responsible for cooking – an alternative to time-consuming meal preparations,' according to the museum. 'The prepackaged TV dinner appealed to busy families because it required little time or effort and yet provided a well-balanced, nutritious meal.' It cost $1 and the company sold ten million within the first year of trading. A 1955 TV ad for the product featured a well-to-do husband speaking to camera: 'My wife never panics. She just takes Swanson TV Turkey Dinners from the freezing compartment of our refrigerator, when I'm a little off schedule ... Mary Lou knows she can have me a swell dinner ready in just 25 minutes. Make your husband lucky too!'

The popularity of the ready meal benefited from changing sociological patterns in the 1960s in America and Britain. More and more people were getting divorced and living alone. The ready meal was a handy, if rather grim and depressing, option for those who lived alone.

Curry became an early staple in the ready meal market because of its easy adaptability to the new format. Batchelors launched its Vesta Curry in 1961 in the UK. Borrowing the technology of space food, this used a dehydration process to preserve the contents and simply required the addition of hot water to prepare the mix of beef, rice and curry sauce. Food writer Mary Gwynn speculates that the Vesta may have been 'the first taste by Britons of "foreign food"'. It was for this reason that early ready meals in the UK were seen as exotic and aspirational, unlike today where there is often a snobbery and disregard for such conveniences. By 1966, half a million Vesta ready meals had been sold by Sainsbury's supermarket alone. Some of those meals had surely been bought by John Lennon, whose favourite dinner was a Vesta Beef Curry. He was said to be particularly fond of slicing a banana into it.

The global ready meal market is due to be worth $143 billion by 2023. In Ireland alone, the chilled ready meal sector is worth €48 million, according to Bord Bia. The ready meal distinguishes itself in this book because of how recent its history is. In spite of this, it appears to be an ever-expanding industry as consumers continue to seek convenience in their lives.

TREAT YOUR KITCHEN

TO AN
ELECTRIC KETTLE

15
THE KETTLE

Americans can't make tea' is a line I have heard many times from returning holiday makers. Many Europeans deplore the addition of a tea bag to warm (as opposed to boiling) water. Readers who have spent any time in the United States will understand the peculiarity of the kettle there. Tea isn't as popular as it is in Britain and Ireland. American homes operate on a lower electrical energy than British homes. American homes, for example, use between 110 and 127 volts, while British homes use between 220 and 240 volts. This means that it takes a kettle longer to boil Stateside than it does here. Kettles are not required for making coffee because many American homes have had automatic percolators for decades.

The kettle is so popular in this part of the world that it plays an important role in the 'TV pickup' phenomenon wherein a surge of demand is placed on the electrical grid during or immediately after major television events. According to British Gas, the largest surge came after England crashed out of the 1986 World Cup. 'Only a nice cup of tea could console the nation. The resulting power surge was the equivalent of 1.12 million kettles being switched on at the same time.'

In the eighteenth century, a power surge also inspired James Watt to dream up a steam engine as a new mode of transport. As a boy, Watt had gazed at his aunt's kettle as the lid rattled and threatened to blow off from the pressure below. Even at this young age he could observe the possible applications of steam in other areas and the kettle was the catalyst in his thought processes.

The evolution of the modern kettle is synonymous with the rise in popularity of tea. The tea leaf arrived in Britain in the seventeenth century. Before its arrival, water was generally boiled in a large cauldron and was used for clearing impurities from drinking water or for cooking purposes. But tea required small amounts of boiled water and making up an enormous cauldron was a waste of time and energy. Therefore, a smaller vessel was required. This led to the development of the kettle as we know it today.

The word kettle is derived from the Latin *catillus,* which originally referred to any lidded saucepan used for cooking. It gradually came to describe a small cauldron with a capacity of up to two litres and with a handle and spout for pouring and for the escape of steam. The lid was essential too as this speeded up the heating process.

Tea was initially an expensive luxury and therefore kettles were often made of silver. In the eighteenth century, kettles would even be brought into drawing rooms as a showpiece. One particular eighteenth century silver kettle, in the collection of the Victoria and Albert Museum in London, has a stand with a spirit burner in the base to keep it hot. 'Tea preparation was one of the few tasks that women or men of the higher stations were proud to be seen to perform themselves,' according to the historians behind *Empire of Tea.* This scene can be seen playing out on a tin-glazed earthenware tea tray, from 1743, in the collection of the V&A. A black servant lugs a large bulbous kettle towards a table of ladies for them to perform their afternoon ritual. The kettle depicted on the tray is remarkably similar to early twentieth century kettles. It has a handle, a lid and a spout in a style which would remain consistent for centuries. When tea became more available to the less privileged classes, copper kettles, which were less expensive yet were excellent conductors, became the norm.

There is some dispute as to who exactly invented the electric kettle. However, we know that two companies, one American and one British, developed prototypes during the early 1890s. Both examples were interesting in the sense that they kept the electrical heating element separate to the water compartment of the kettle, for safety reasons. The idea of mixing electricity and water was understandably terrifying to early adopters of the new technology. This meant that the boiling process was slow. The kettle developed by the Carpenter Electric Company in Chicago, for example, took twelve minutes to boil. It would be another 30 years before an engineer managed to successfully and safely integrate the heating element with water. Birmingham engineers Bulpitt and Sons encased the heating element within a waterproof metal tube and with this innovation they launched the Swan Kettle in 1922.

Although rural electrification only began in Ireland from 1946, the availability of electric products did exist in major urban centres much earlier. The ESB (Electricity Supply Board) began an advertising campaign for their first kettle in the late 1920s. An ad in the *Irish Independent* gives a fascinating insight into just how unfamiliar and exotic a device like this was at the time. 'An electric kettle gives boiling water at any time in any room with a convenience outlet ... The water is boiled quickly, cheaply and with the absolute cleanliness of electricity. No smoke, no fumes, no ashes to clear away – you don't even have to light a match.' The kettle cost 35 shillings, which would be the equivalent of €90 today, a considerable investment at the time.

▲ EIGHTEENTH CENTURY KETTLE WITH SPIRIT BURNER.
© VICTORIA AND ALBERT MUSEUM, LONDON

The electric kettle remained an expensive luxury right into the following decade. In 1939 the *Cork Examiner* investigated the provision of electric kettles in courthouses around the county. The report cites a letter from the county registrar to Cork County Council which reads, 'With further reference to the provision of a heater in the various courthouses for the purpose of boiling a kettle for the judge's lunch, he has suggested to me that if he was provided with an electric kettle this would obviate the expense of installing a heater in each courthouse'. The request was denied by the council.

▲ ADVERTISEMENT FOR THE RUSSELL HOBBS K2 KETTLE, 1959

However, one major hurdle had yet to be overcome in the evolution of this kitchen staple. Nowadays, we take it for granted that we can switch on a kettle and then wander off and do a pee, safe in the knowledge that the kettle won't burn the house down. Before automatic kettles arrived they had to be watched and switched off manually after boiling. Once the kettle boiled there was nothing to stop the heating element from continuing to burn, causing unattended kettles to boil dry, melt or even cause a fire.

Many attempts were made to solve the problem. For example, the Chadeau electric kettle of the 1940s featured a sprung rod which would expand when heated and consequently push the plug out. This was a hopeful fix at best. The search for a failsafe solution continued. Step forward Mr. Bill Russell and Mr. Peter Hobbs ... these two English gentlemen, salesman and inventor respectively, changed the kettle forever when they launched the K1 in 1955, the world's first fully automatic kettle.

Russell and Hobbs had introduced a bimetallic strip to their product. This is a brilliantly simple piece of technology. It contains two different types of metal which heat at different speeds, causing the strip to bend as a result. As the kettle heated up, the bimetallic strip started to curve, eventually breaking the circuit and shutting off the electric feed. Finally, the kettle had become automatic and safe.

Russell Hobbs became the market leader during the 1960s. Their K2 kettle, a sleeker version of the 1956 model (and now a design icon) became a staple on wedding lists. It cost about £7 in the late 1960s which is £113 in today's money. The company introduced the world's first plastic kettle, the Futura 3510 (which sounds like a Nokia phone from the late '90s), in 1972, vastly reducing the cost. It was made with a heat resistant plastic called noryl which had been developed by General Electric back in the mid-1960s.

The adoption of plastic made the electric kettle cheaper and more affordable to all classes, establishing it as a kitchen staple forevermore.

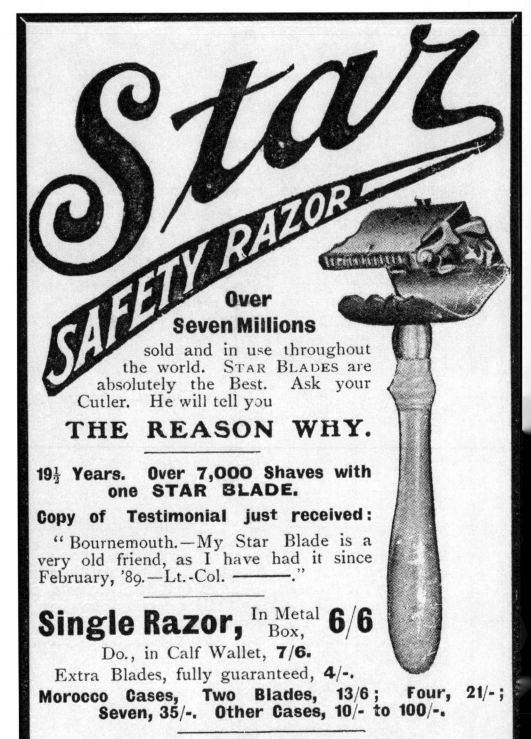

Star

SAFETY RAZOR

Over Seven Millions

sold and in use throughout the world. STAR BLADES are absolutely the Best. Ask your Cutler. He will tell you

THE REASON WHY.

19½ Years. Over 7,000 Shaves with one STAR BLADE.

Copy of Testimonial just received:

" Bournemouth.—My Star Blade is a very old friend, as I have had it since February, '89.—Lt.-Col. ———."

Single Razor, In Metal Box, **6/6**

Do., in Calf Wallet, **7/6.**

Extra Blades, fully guaranteed, **4/-.**

Morocco Cases, Two Blades, 13/6; Four, 21/-; Seven, 35/-. Other Cases, 10/- to 100/-.

Write at once for Illustrated Catalogue.

MARKT & CO. (LONDON), Ltd., Razor Dept., 6, CITY ROAD, LONDON.

Of all Cutlers, Silversmiths, or High-class Chemists.

THE RAZOR

In Ancient Rome, a young man's first shave was celebrated with a religious ceremony called the *despositio barbae*. The shorn bristles would be offered as a gift to the gods. Grooming was an important aspect of Roman life. Slaves were permitted to have beards, as a way to distinguish them from citizens, but politicians would be refused entry to the senate unless they were clean shaven. It was for these reasons that the *despositio barbae* represented a milestone in a man's life, an event which drew family and friends to gather and mark the occasion, much like an 18th or 21st birthday party today.

Wealthy Romans had barbers, or *tonsors* as they were known, as part of their household staff. Tonsors used a razor called a *novacila*, a flat blade made of iron, often fitted with three holes in the handle for the fingers to grip. This was spat on and sharpened on a whetstone. But it was primitive and much blunter than modern razors, often causing painful cuts, despite the application of soap or oil to the face prior to shaving. Tonsors would plaster shaving cuts with spiders' webs mixed in vinegar to stop the bleeding and heal the wound.

Alexander the Great had inspired cosmetic culture in Rome with his own shaving rituals. He had insisted that his troops shave their beards so as to prevent the enemy from having something to grab on to during hand-to-hand combat. But Alexander also saw himself as a demigod and appearing clean-shaven played into his vanity. 'Because the artists of his day depicted mythic heroes like Achilles and Heracles as eternally youthful and beardless, he shaved himself and encouraged his followers to do the same,' explains Christopher Oldstone-Moore in *Of Beards and Men*. Roman soldiers rubbed their facial hair off using a pumice stone, a type of coarse volcanic rock which creates a friction with the skin and helps remove the hair.

The beardless generation came to an end with the arrival of Emperor Hadrian. He used his beard as a way to cover up an unsightly facial scar. As we see so many times in this book, fashions, in history at least, tend to filter down from the top. Hadrian's inferiors wished to emulate his style and so the beard became popular again.

During the Middle Ages, beards were frowned upon by the Catholic Church. They were seen as unclean and, perhaps more importantly, being clean-shaven was seen as a way of distinguishing yourself from Jewish and Muslim men who often wore beards. In fact, in 1096, the Archbishop of Rouen went the whole hog and instituted an official ban on beards. Anyone who turned up at mass with a few days of growth, after a heavy session the night before no doubt, was threatened with excommunication. That can't have helped a hangover. The Christian endorsement of shaving led to an explosion in barber shops in Europe in the Medieval period. By the sixteenth century, however, it had become acceptable to grow one's facial hair again, as evidenced by the luxurious white beard of Pope Sixtus V in a portrait housed in the Vatican.

Shaving was a dangerous activity prior to the introduction of the safety razor. The application of a blade to the sensitive and thin skin of the face required a delicate touch. Self-shaving was considered too dangerous and men felt compelled to visit a professional barber. The advent of home shaving was brought about with the introduction of new safety mechanisms. Much of the history of the razor from the eighteenth century onwards involves the innovation of master cutlers, men who already worked with sharp metals.

◄ LORD NELSON'S RAZOR, MADE OF HORN
AND STEEL. WELLCOME COLLECTION

French cutler Jean Jacques Perret invented one of the world's first safety razors in 1762. He even wrote a book about shaving, *L'Art D'Apprendre a se Raser Soi-Meme* (The Art of Shaving Oneself) and eventually presented his invention to Louis XVI in 1779. 'Inspired by a carpenter's plane, it consisted of a wooden sleeve that enclosed the blade of a folding straight razor, allowing only a small portion of the edge to protrude, thus preventing one from accidentally slicing off a portion of one's ear,' writes Robert Waits in *Before Gilette*. Perret's razor was widely manufactured and gained great popularity in the late eighteenth century. The French had also invented the shaving brush, using stiff badger hair, at around the same time, helping to make the entire shaving process easier to do at home.

It comes as no surprise that Sheffield, the home of steel cutlery, also became synonymous with the razor industry. By the mid-eighteenth century, Benjamin Huntsman was producing the new and superior cast steel in Sheffield, made using the crucible process. This was then used in folding straight razors (also called cut-throat razors). The advantage of Huntsman's new steel was that it was stronger and therefore better able to sustain a very thin edge. A desire for thin blades is understandable, especially as razor manufacturers began to experiment with V-shaped wedge blades and thinner 'hollow grind' versions.

The Kampfe brothers, three German immigrants working in New York City, patented the Star razor in 1880. They had been expert cutlery manufacturers before turning their skills to the emerging safety razor market. The Star is important for a number of reasons. In design terms it represented the growing

▲ KAMPFE BROS, STAR SINGLE EDGE SAFETY RAZOR. MADE IN USA, CIRCA 1900S

popularity of the hoe-shaped razor, much like today's most popular products. The patent stated that 'the refuse matter ... will be retained within the hollow holder permitting the use of the device without danger of soiling the fingers of the user'. This was a specially designed 'lather catcher' which scooped up excess residue as you glided the blade across your face.

The 1897 Sears catalogue lists the beautifully decorative Star razor, made of nickel-plated steel, for $1.50 (about $46 in today's money) and describes it as 'an invention which obviates all danger of cutting the face. It ... is indispensable to travellers, miners and persons camping out'. The adverts at the turn of the century attempted to lure customers away from the barber and persuade consumers that home shaving was now safe. 'Shave yourself ... it is a pleasure with the genuine Star Safety Razor,' reads one ad. 'Every man his own barber!' says another. By 1899, five million Stars had been sold.

The arrival of the disposable razor was an attempt to make life more convenient for men, but also a cunning way to multiply a manufacturer's profits. The blade in the Star razor had to be removed regularly for stropping in order to keep it sharp. A Baltimore salesman by the name of King C. Gillette was inspired to develop a disposable razor blade, meaning each shave was conducted with a perfectly sharp edge. Gillette had been encouraged by a friend of his who had developed a disposable bottle cap. The business model was game changing: a disposable product creates a constant stream of repeat custom.

Gillette teamed up with William Nickerson, an engineer from MIT, to develop what would eventually become a global brand. 'They improved on the safety razor by producing a double-edge blade cut from a template which could be dropped into the top of a T-shape razor, then used, discarded, and more importantly, replaced over and over,' says Peterkin. Nickerson played a crucial role in finding a way to mass produce the thin steel blades at a reasonable price. In 1903, his first year of production, Gillette sold a paltry 51 razors. The following year he sold 90,000 and sales of his disposable razor increased exponentially from then onwards. During World War One, the US army placed an order for 3.5 million Gillette razors, cementing the company as a market leader.

In the early decades of Gillette, the company used advertising to persuade men that daily shaving was an absolute necessity, and that failure to do so would also lead to failure in life. A 1932 ad shows a man with a few days' growth on his face, breaking some bad news to his wife. 'I didn't get the job,' he says. Another declared, 'The man who doesn't keep clean shaven is never welcome'. They even went so far as to suggest that a man's romantic prospects would be endangered if he didn't shave. 'No woman cares to entertain or be seen with a man who neglects shaving ... failure to shave carefully is an affront that women simply will not overlook.'

In 1916 Gillette recognised the potential of the female market, at a time when women were being encouraged to use depilatory creams to deal with unwanted hair. The 14 karat gold-plated Milady Décolleté came in a beautiful ivory box, lined with velvet and satin. It was an expensive luxury however, at $5 a pop ($115 in today's money). Early advertisements exploited the emerging culture of shame regarding women's body hair. They promised that it would 'solve an embarrassing personal problem' and that it is 'welcomed by women everywhere, now that a feature of good dressing and good grooming is to keep the underarm white and smooth'.

1950S AMERICAN SUPERMARKET

THE SUPERMARKET

When I travel to a foreign country I try and visit a supermarket during my time there. Supermarkets are museums of domestic life. They are a window into the way we live, what we eat and drink, how we clean, our cosmetic practices, and even what goes on in our bathrooms. I remember visiting a Walmart in Savannah in the United States and being astonished by the multiple varieties of aerosol cheese on display, a demonstration of modern America's ability to reduce foods to their most convenient form: a spray. A small supermarket I visited in Cuba had just one brandless toilet paper because of the absence of competition in a communist system. In Ireland, toilet paper products can take up an entire aisle with everything from cheap sandpaper to luxury quilts that promise to kiss the bottom clean.

A supermarket I discovered in the United Arab Emirates was completely absent of pork products and alcohol, reflecting a strict adherence to Islamic dietary laws. In fact, I was intrigued to find a separate and secluded area in the shop for 'Non Muslims' in which items containing pork *were* for sale. Everything from ham to confectionary containing gelatin were stored here, a little oasis of pork for Westerners.

These three experiences speak to the diversity of supermarkets around the world, each responding to different sets of cultural requirements.

The modern supermarket hosts an extraordinary variety of food within a relatively small space. 'Air-conditioned, odourless, illuminated by fluorescent buzzing tubes, the American supermarket doesn't present itself as having very much to do with nature. And yet what is this place if not a landscape (manmade, it's true) teeming with plants and animals?' wonders Michael Pollan in *The Omnivore's Dilemma*. Perhaps the supermarket best represents man's subjugation of nature. It is in this place that we have cut up and packaged animals and plants, a showroom of our control over the natural world. Yet despite all this, the teeming modern supermarket had humble beginnings.

Before the advent of the supermarket, shoppers visited grocery stores and asked a clerk for the items on their shopping list. These were retrieved, weighed out and wrapped. It was a laborious, time-consuming and expensive model to run. American entrepreneur Clarence Saunders changed the world when he opened his first Piggly Wiggly on Jefferson street in Memphis, Tennessee in 1916. Piggly Wiggly is today an enormous chain of supermarkets in the Deep South and Midwest of the United States, but Saunders' ideas were revolutionary at the time. His vision was to create a self-service operation which was a faster and more efficient way of shopping.

He designed his store so that once customers entered they would follow the four aisles until they eventually ended up at the checkout. Shoppers could rent a wooden basket for three cents, which they were then required to leave in the store once they finished. He organised groceries according to category to make the experience easier for shoppers. Because it was self-service, he was able to reduce the number of clerks in his employment.

A very early advertisement for the new shopping experience used wry humour to try and explain how his shop worked. 'The Piggly Wiggly knows its own business best and its business will be this: To have no store clerks gab and smirk while folks are standing around ten deep to get waited on. Every customer will be her own clerk, so if she wants to talk to a can of tomatoes and kill her time, alright and well.'

Saunders' vision was so bold at the time that at first his competitors simply wrote him off. 'Other grocery men laughed at Saunders when they heard of his arrangement of the Piggly Wiggly,' writes Mike Freeman in his biography of the great supermarket pioneer. 'No one in Memphis had seen anything like it. They said he was crazy ... There was no one to wait on customers. No one to carry the

▲ PIGGLY WIGGLY, THE WORLD'S FIRST SUPERMARKET

bags home for them. How could anyone keep loyal shoppers in a grocery store like that?'

In the store's first week, a customer arrived in and asked for a pound of butter. She was cordially directed to the appropriate aisle but she demanded that the clerk retrieve it for her. Under strict instructions from Saunders not to pick up items for the shoppers, the woman left the Piggly Wiggly in a huff. However, within a month of opening his first store he had already opened two more in response to demand. Saunders patented his idea and began issuing franchises around the country, establishing a new trend in shopping.

The Great Depression, followed by World War Two, had an enormous impact on the growth of supermarkets in America. 'Price became the all-important factor in where consumers chose to shop,' according to Andrew F. Smith in *Eating*

History. 'Shoppers were willing to forego the pleasant atmosphere and personal attention of a small grocery store for the chill, cavernous supermarket with its lower prices.' This led to the closure of thousands of small grocery shops and the beginning of the end of a certain type of consumer culture. In the post-war period the supermarket flourished. During the 1940s, an average American supermarket housed roughly 3,000 different types of product, but by the mid-50s, this figure had doubled.

However, the supermarket remained an American peculiarity. The *Scotsman* newspaper ran a feature in 1947 about a supermarket the journalist had visited while on a trip to the States, with the headline 'New American wonder of the world'. It described the new phenomenon with reverence: 'Since everyone pushes around their own wire basket-on-wheels, picking out what they want at random, there is a meditative hush ... there is no need to talk'.

Queen Elizabeth, during a visit to the United States in 1957 to meet President Eisenhower, passed a supermarket during her convoy and asked to stop and visit the oddity which she had never seen before. The Associated Press reported that 'one woman almost dropped her groceries when the Queen spoke to her. That was when her majesty, bemused by the grocery cart's little collapsible seat for small fry, beamed: "It is particularly nice to be able to bring your children here"'.

Before the 1960s, Irish shopping was dominated by two chains of grocery store, Findlaters and Leverett & Frye. Ireland's first supermarket was H. Williams and Co. on Henry Street in Dublin. It opened in 1959 and the company went on to have many outlets around the country. However, things really kicked off when 23-year-old Feargal Quinn opened his first supermarket on Clanbrassil Street in Dundalk in November 1960.

Quinn had travelled to France previously in order to learn how supermarkets worked. In a 2009 interview with *Trinity News* Quinn remembered his Eureka moment: 'In France, they had a fantastic thing called self-service, where if one wanted to get, say a magazine, you would go to the shelf and pick one out yourself. In Ireland, that didn't happen and you had to ask the person at the till to get your magazine from behind the counter'. He called his new enterprise Quinn Supermarket, becoming Superquinn in 1970, in order to differentiate it from its rival, Quinnsworth.

Quinn bought the 210 sq/m site (¾ the size of a tennis court) in Dundalk for £10,000 and he employed eight staff. He didn't have shopping trolleys in 1960 but he did provide shopping baskets. These caused many problems because the customers kept using them to bring their groceries home. Customers were amazed that they had to leave them at the door. Feargal Quinn was the first to pipe music through his shops and he had a microphone to advertise special deals to his customers. Shopping in Ireland would never be the same again.

1950S TOASTER

18
THE TOASTER

Why do we 'have a toast' when drinking? The celebratory toast has its origins in actual toasted bread. 'In the Middle Ages slices of toast soaked in wine, water or broth, called sops, were often used as ways to add heat, flavor, and calories,' writes Dan Jurafsky in *The Language of Food*. In Shakespeare's *The Merry Wives of Windsor* Falstaff says, 'Go fetch me a quart of sack (wine); put a toast in't'. Over time, a toast came to describe the activity of honouring somebody. 'Frequently these toasts were made to the health of a lady ... she flavored the party just as the spiced toast flavored the wine. Popular ladies ... became the "toast of the town",' says Jurafsky. As a result of this relationship between toasted bread and alcohol, we continue to toast our guests to this day, albeit without the accompaniment of bread.

Before the nineteenth century, toast was indeed a common food, but it was made using either a long metal fork which held a slice of bread over a fire or a wire rack which held it in place on a stove. The end of the Victorian era saw the development of electric machines especially engineered to toast bread. Scottish scientist Alan MacMasters invented the world's first electric toaster in 1893. The Eclipse consisted of a vertical rack which held a single slice of bread. Electricity was passed through iron wiring to toast it. The slice needed to be turned over to brown both sides as there was only one heating element. It wasn't a success. Iron wiring melted easily and was a fire hazard. Also, few homes had electricity in the 1890s so perhaps MacMasters was a little ahead of his time.

The American metallurgist Albert Marsh made safe toasting machines possible when he developed nichrome, in 1905. 'He mixed nickel with metals in the chromium group,' explains Ed Sobey in *The Way Kitchens Work*. This created 'an alloy with a high melting point, a low rate of oxidation (formation of rust) and an electrical resistance 50 times that of copper'. This high resistance helped to create heat, yet it was still safe because it didn't burn out. Marsh's heating element would be applied to many different appliances but it found its first home in the electric toaster.

At first, toasters were used solely in the hotel and restaurant trade. General Electric launched the first commercially successful toaster for the home, the D-12, in 1909. The D-12 is a curious object. Safety required its four nichrome heating elements to be set into an ugly cage, which the designers softened with a beautiful floral ceramic base. Two slices of bread could fit on either side of the elements. Again, the bread had to be flipped to toast both sides and it had to be manually switched on and off, but it was an enormous leap forward. What came out of the machine came to be known as 'electric toast.'

MODEL D12 ELECTRIC TOASTER, 1910

In an article in a 1913 edition of *American Homes and Gardens*, the writer ponders the introduction of electrical conveniences. 'We are all compelled to eat three times a day ... and on someone's shoulders falls the burden of preparation. In these days of the help problem, this burden many times falls upon the housewife herself. She it is, who will welcome the attractive electrical appliances.' The toaster arrived at a time when domestic service was beginning to disappear and the 'big house' was in decline. For the wealthy who could afford early toasters, these appliances represented a new way of operating a household with ever diminishing numbers of servants. The writer becomes positively giddy about toasters when she says, 'Think of the fun one can have making toast at the breakfast table, each one buttering the crisp fresh pieces as they come from such a toaster, instead of getting red-faced and heated over the stove'. To make them as convenient as possible (and perhaps to show them off) people actually kept the toaster on the dining table, as opposed to the kitchen counter. An advertisement for Ediswan electric toasters in the *Irish Press* in 1933 states, 'Makes two pieces of delicious crisp toast in three minutes. A useful and attractive addition to the breakfast table'.

The Walter Genther Company's 1926 Toastmaster was the first to feature a pop-up mechanism. Mechanic and Minnesota native Charles Strite was fed up with the burnt toast in his work canteen and set about creating the spring mechanism which we still use today. It featured a lever for starting the timer and another to lower the bread and ignite the electrical current. A third lever set the shade of the bread. This allowed users to predetermine just how brown they wanted their toast.

Marketed as an 'automatic toaster' one advertisement for the Toastmaster read, 'You do not have to watch it. The toast can't burn'. Another ad claimed that 'it is so completely automatic that it even discharges the toast when done – and then shuts off its own current'. In reality, the Toastmaster took a while to warm up. The instruction manual even advised using it without bread for a couple of minutes in the morning to get the heating element going. Then it got hotter and hotter the more it was used. Despite these glitches, it was a major commercial success. It cost $12.50 (about $180 in today's money), so it was a considerable investment for consumers who could simply buy a non-automatic toaster for around $2. The Toastmaster was the first machine with the heating elements encased, making

**TOASTMASTER**

Automatic Electric Toaster

You do not have to Watch it~ The Toast can't Burn.

Study Carefully These **INSTRUCTIONS**

THE TOASTMASTER

it much safer to use. Covered in shiny nickel, the Toastmaster became an icon of sleek Art Deco design. By 1930 half a million had been sold across the US.

The arrival of sliced bread in the late 1920s boosted the fortunes of the toaster. Missouri native Otto Rohwedder developed a 5-foot-long 'power-driven multi bladed bread slicer' which could automatically produce a sliced pan. Initially bakers were highly sceptical of Rohwedder's innovation. 'Few people in the industry believed that bread could be automatically sliced as it came off the assembly line,' explains Aaron Bobrow-Strain in his social history, *White Bread*. 'Bread was too unruly. What would hold the sliced loaves together? How would slicing affect the chemistry of taste? What would prevent sliced bread from rapidly molding or staling?'

Rohwedder set out to confront all these obstacles. Initially he used pins to keep the sliced loaves from falling apart, until he eventually patented a bread wrapping machine which solved the issue. Rohwedder pitched his idea to Frank Bench of the Chillicothe Baking Company in Missouri. Bench was struggling to make ends meet and his bakery was facing bankruptcy. However, he decided to take a punt on Rohwedder's machine in 1928. The result was Kleen-Maid bread, the world's first sliced pan. Within weeks Bench's sales had exploded by 2,000 per cent. Soon, the craze for sliced bread captured the nation. Rohwedder's timing was perfect. The toaster was spreading into homes across the country just as he introduced a mechanism for creating customised slices for these machines.

In 1943 the US government banned sliced bread in an effort to save on the enormous amount of steel required to make slicing machines. This led to a public backlash and within two months sliced bread was back, with the *New York Times* commenting, 'Housewives who have risked thumbs and tempers slicing bread at home ... will find sliced loaves back on the grocery shelves tomorrow'.

Although the toaster began life as an expensive luxury for the few, it is now a cheap essential. In 2018, 17 million toaster units were sold in the United States alone.

NILS BOHLIN MODELLING HIS 3-POINT SEAT BELT, 1950S

THE SEAT BELT

Ford Motors introduced a seat belt as an optional extra for their customers in 1956. This was a public relations disaster. After running an advertising campaign claiming that 'You'll drive safer ever after!', their competitor, General Motors, made no mention of safety features at all. Even though they did in fact offer seat belts, GM focused their advertising instead on style and power. Ford's campaign backfired. Consumers presumed that Ford cars must be dangerous if they required such safety measures and other cars didn't. Sales plummeted and GM got the upper hand.

Henry Ford II decried, '(We are) selling safety, but Chevrolet is selling cars'. The following year Ford were forced to change tack. In his memoirs, Lee Iacocca, the legendary Ford executive best known for developing the iconic Mustang, recalled, 'We spent millions of dollars and gave it everything we had, but the public didn't even stir. We developed the hardware, we advertised, promoted and demonstrated it, and we couldn't give the stuff away. We had customers saying things like: "Sure, I'll take the car, but you'll have to take out those seat belts or I'm not interested"'.

The Ford case epitomises the massive challenges inherent in winning the public around to the benefits of the seat belt. Consumers were suspicious of it and often felt it was an unnecessary nuisance. In the 1965 film *Thunderball*, James Bond demurs when villainess Fiona Volpe suggests he use a seat belt. Such protective measures were seen as unmanly.

The staggering rise in road deaths in the opening decades of the twentieth century led medical professionals to call on car manufacturers to implement more safety measures. In 1910 there were just over 1,000 fatalities on roads in the United States, but by 1930 there were 31,000.

One of the leading physicians calling for change in the industry was a plastic surgeon from Detroit by the name of Claire Straith (Claire was clearly also a man's name at that time). He proclaimed, 'What I consider one of the most pertinent problems of present-day medicine is the proper care and management of the ever-growing numbers of victims of motor car accidents. The ability of the engineer to design, and of the industrialist to make easily available, ever-speedier motor vehicles far surpasses the intellectual ability of the average man to utilize them safely'.

As a plastic surgeon, Straith had become used to treating victims of car accidents. 'He recognised that the hard steel interiors of automobiles – their knobs, handles and protrusions – and their glass, contributed significantly to injury and death. He actively sought seat belts as standard in automobiles,' according to Paul Josephson in *Traffic*.

Manufacturers slowly began to respond to safety concerns in the late 1940s. Nash Motors, a manufacturer from Wisconsin, which eventually went out of business, was the first to introduce a seat belt, in 1949. These were two-point belts or 'lap belts' as they were popularly known at the time. They wrapped across the driver's waist but offered no support to the upper body. They were deeply unpopular with buyers and some reportedly tore them out of their cars.

There was a whole mythology of disaster related to the wearing of seat belts. People thought that they would cause you to be trapped in a car in the event of an accident or that the impact of a collision would cause the belt to injure the abdomen. It was reported that just two percent of buyers actually used their seat belts in the entire fleet of 48,000 Nash cars sold in 1949. The following year the company discontinued them.

The mid-twentieth century saw enormous change in America's transport network. In 1956 President Dwight Eisenhower launched his interstate road system. Over the following twenty years a staggering 74,000 kilometres of roads would be built to link every state in the country. This infrastructure was, of

3-POINT SEAT BELT

course, matched by an explosion in the numbers of cars using these roads. Safety inevitably became a more and more pressing issue. The three-point seat belt would eventually become the standard bearer in this area.

Three men were responsible for the modern three-point seat belt, two introducing it into America and one into Europe, at roughly the same time. American engineers Roger Griswold and Hugh De Haven invented and patented the world's first three-point belt in 1951. This seat belt linked the two hips and the chest and is similar to the modern one we use today. This meant that the upper body was supported, not just the lower body, spreading the pressure of impact. However, their innovation was problematic. Much like a helicopter harness, the buckle was in the centre of the body which was uncomfortable and required two hands to connect.

Nils Bohlin, an engineer working for Volvo in Sweden, perfected the three-point belt in 1958 and is often credited as the father of car safety. Bohlin, who had previously worked in the aircraft industry, approached the design of the seat belt from a human needs perspective. He understood that people found the whole idea tedious, so he set about creating a belt which could be fastened with one hand, just like the one we use today. He said, 'The pilots I worked with in the aerospace industry were willing to put on almost anything to keep them safe in case of a crash, but regular people in cars don't want to be uncomfortable even for a minute'.

Bohlin's design anchored the belt on either side of the seat, drawing the strands together into a V-shape so that the belt didn't shift while in use. Unsure of the demand for such an innovation, initially Volvo only introduced the belt into the Swedish market. However, by 1963 they had rolled it out internationally, cementing their reputation for safety.

In 1968, Bohlin was brought to the United States to speak about his seat belt at the Consumer Products Safety Commission. By the end of the year manufacturers were obliged to include three-point belts in their cars. The public were still not convinced, however. By 1980 just 15% of Americans actually used seat belts, even if they were pre-installed.

Despite the alarming number of road deaths each year, governments remained slow to introduce legislation that would enforce the wearing of seat belts. The

Australian state of Victoria led the world in 1970 when they made it the law to wear seat belts while driving.

In 1971 manufacturers were obliged to install seat belts for cars in the Irish market. However, government research showed that only five percent of drivers actually used them. Authorities realised that they needed to be enforced. Ireland made it obligatory for drivers to buckle up in 1979, four years before the UK.

It is interesting to contrast the number of road deaths in 1970s Ireland compared with today. For example, in 1978 there were 627 fatalities on Irish roads, while in 2018 there were 148. Of course this isn't all down to the humble seat belt but it has certainly made a significant difference. Volvo estimates that Bohlin's seat belt has saved over a million lives since it was first introduced in the 1950s.

HOTCHKISS NO. 1, LATE NINETEENTH CENTURY

THE STAPLER

Exasperated co-workers commonly prowl office floors looking for their missing staplers. People plaster their names across them in Tipp-Ex and send angry 'to everyone' emails when they go walkabout. 'He's put my stapler inside jelly again,' howls Gareth in Ricky Gervais's *The Office* after Tim makes a mess of his desk. The writers are mocking the pettiness of workplace culture and the mundane ubiquity of one of the most enduring administrative tools of the past 150 years. Despite the vast digitalisation of office life, the stapler is one of the few trusty devices which hasn't been swept into the dustbin of history.

We assume that a stapler will work efficiently every time we pick it up to fasten a bundle of papers together. Although it appears to be a simple piece of technology, its evolution from the 1860s to the 1930s illustrates the complicated series of actions that need to be perfectly executed in order for the stapler to deliver a perfect staple every time.

These mechanics are best articulated in an advertisement in an American magazine in 1907 which describes the Hotchkiss No. 1 as an 'automatic paper fastener.' It could be loaded with 25 staples. 'These staples, when inserted into the machine, are automatically cut off and fed forward, accurately and without failure. The staple is always ready to be driven and a single blow will drive it through 1 to 25 sheets of paper.' The Hotchkiss required such force to drive the plunger through paper that office workers often used a mallet.

It is no coincidence that the stapler is a late nineteenth century invention. It confronted an increasing need for technology which could help to organise vast amounts of paperwork. 'The second half of the nineteenth century witnessed a profound transformation in American offices,' argues Sean P. Philips in *Technical Innovation in American History*. 'As the country expanded westward, land, railroad, telegraph – and soon telephone – offices required efficient means for creating, organizing and distributing paperwork as well as tabulating and recording finances and accounts.'

Among the earliest forms of paper fastener, long before the stapler was even a pipe dream, was red tape. King Charles V of Spain is thought to have introduced this influential administrative system in the sixteenth century, according to political scientist *Del Dickson* in *The People's Government: An Introduction to Democracy*. 'Red symbolized royal power and wealth (the dye was exorbitantly expensive). Routine administrative dossiers, in contrast, were bound with plain cloth ribbon.'

Others believe that red ribbon was used to organise Henry VIII's petitions to the Vatican, requesting the annulment of his marriage to Catherine of Aragon. The OED places the origins of the expression later, in the eighteenth century. The word *tape* itself derives from the Old English 'tæppe', meaning a piece of cloth or ribbon, which could be used for tying or measuring things. Whatever the case, the concept of red tape eventually came to describe the tedium of bureaucracy. By the nineteenth century, all manner of fasteners were used to organise paper records, from the stitching of thread or silk twist to the use of straight pins. None of these were efficient. Stitching was time consuming and pins were finicky and dangerous for the fingers.

American George McGill patented the first stapler in 1867. This was a brass contraption which punched a small hole in a stack of papers. A fastener was then inserted by hand. In 1879 he patented an improved version called the Single-Stroke Staple Press. Weighing just over a kilogram in weight, it was made from cast iron and steel. Individual staples had to be inserted each time the device was used, according to the Early Office Museum, which features a fascinating catalogue of early staplers.

A patent war erupted a year later when another organisation called the Philadelphia Novelty Manufacturing Company launched their Novelty Paper Fastener. This stapler featured an alarming eight-inch plunger designed to ram the staple through a stack of papers. Early versions required the user to bend the legs of the staple manually, but by 1882 it came with an anvil which clinched the staple's legs automatically. McGill believed that his patent rights were being infringed upon. 'There then began an over two-year, bare-knuckle battle of the major stapler manufacturers,' according to historical office equipment collector Frank Parsons. It doesn't appear that the dispute was ever properly resolved and both manufacturers continued to build their sales revenue.

When the Hotchkiss No 1 was launched in 1896, it was one of the earliest devices to feature a strip of staples. Before this time, staples had to be inserted individually for each use. The Hotchkiss had a curling tail or 'spiral coil' of staples which fed directly into the mechanism. While this was a step forward, it still required considerable force to break the staples off their metal coil. It cost $1.25 in 1901 (this included 500 staplers), which would equate to roughly $37 today. I managed to procure an original Hotchkiss a couple of years ago. Despite its 120 years of service, it remains solid as a bull. Its decorative cast iron modelling makes it a design classic.

In 1905 the Hotchkiss No 3 was developed as an antidote to the rather violent experience of the plunger models. It featured a compression lever rather than a plunger. One catalogue said 'it operates noiselessly and is especially desirable if one objects to or cannot stand the effects of the concussion on the hands in the "blow" styles'. The Hotchkiss staplers were so successful that the common word for stapler in Japanese is *hotchikisu*.

Two further innovations helped define the modern stapler. Firstly, in 1927 Hotchkiss began using 'frozen' staples, a strip of staples that were 'lead fastened' together. These sticks of staples could be loaded into a magazine and they were much easier to separate from each other. In 1925 Jack Linksy established the Parrot Speed Fastener Company. This would later be renamed Swingline, one of the world's leading stapler manufacturers to this day. He further developed the magazine model by using a fine adhesive to stick the individual staples together. But his unique contribution to the technology came with the Speed Stapler in 1937. It contained a spring-loaded mechanism in the magazine which propelled the staples forward automatically. This innovation is still used in almost all staplers to this day.

ACTOR REG VARNEY USES THE
WORLD'S FIRST ATM, LONDON, 1967

THE AUTOMATIC TELLER MACHINE

The ATM, or automatic teller machine, was born out of a 1960s craze for automation and self-service. It was part of a new culture of convenience. Although Scottish engineer John Shepherd-Barron is credited with inventing the world's first ATM, the reality is that a number of banks in the UK, Sweden and the United States were simultaneously searching for a way to allow customers access to their money outside of business hours. Wealthy customers already had cheque books, but there was a desire to find a way to make cash available all day and all night.

The *Daily Mirror* framed the arrival of 'instant cash' machines in a 1967 article as a way for banks to drum up more business, saying the devices give 'a fair idea of the banks' drive to capture those two in three adults in Britain who still don't have a bank account'. Another newspaper called it a ploy to deal with the 'Saturday opening battle'. At that time there was enormous pressure in the UK from the banking unions to close branches at the weekends. Emerging technologies such as the ATM offered a way to do business without needing to have staff on the ground.

Shepherd-Barron is said to have come up with the idea for the ATM when he was in the bath, a place that has inspired more than one

'Eureka' moment over the centuries. During an interview with the BBC in 2007 to celebrate his invention's 40th anniversary, he said, 'It struck me (that) there must be a way I could get my own money anywhere in the world or the UK. I hit upon the idea of a chocolate bar dispenser, but replacing chocolate with cash'.

He brought his vending machine idea to Barclays Bank who installed his ATM at their Enfield branch on June 27th, 1967. A plaque memoralises the ATM to this day on Enfield High Street. Archival newspaper photographs show huge crowds gathered at the ATM for the launch, everyone trying to catch a glimpse of this ode to the future. Actor Reg Varney, famous at the time for his BBC sitcom *Beggar My Neighbour*, was granted the honour of being the first user of the machine.

Much like today's ATMs, Sheperd-Barron's machine was a steel rectangle set into a hole in the wall. Instead of a screen it had two drawers and a keypad. The user placed a paper token, impregnated with carbon 14 (a radioactive substance detectable by the machine's technology) into the drawer. Although this sounds mildly alarming, Shepherd-Barron claimed that you would have to lick 136,000 of these tokens for the radioactive substance to have an effect on you.

For security purposes, the customer then entered a four-digit number into the keypad which matched with their token ID. His wife had advised him on a four-digit number over dinner one night as she said she wouldn't be able to remember more than that. A simple chat over the dinner table helped develop the now ubiquitous PIN code. The second drawer dispensed a £10 note, the only monitory option available. This would be worth around £175 in today's money and was 'quite enough for a wild weekend,' according to Shepherd-Barron.

The first bank to introduce a plastic card for use in their ATMs was the Chemical Bank of New York, in 1969. Donald Wetzel, who held the first patent for an ATM in America, came up with the idea of the card. It was encoded with a magnetic strip and was unique to each customer. In an interview with the National Museum of American History, Wetzel said that using cards and ATMs was a way for banks to engage with modern, younger customers. But perfecting the technology of the ATM card was tricky. 'We had a machine, and if you just hand made some plastic cards, the machine would work, but if you went to a manufacturer and asked him to run off 5,000 cards for you, most of them didn't work.'

Eventually, after much trial and error, he managed to produce a machine that could reliably read ATM cards. This was a massive step forward in the evolution of the ATM. The Chemical Bank launched Wetzel's machine with the advertising slogan, 'On September 2nd, our banks will open at 9am and never close again'.

INTERNAL STRUCTRE OF THE ATM

There were hiccups of course, like with any new technology. Rain was the number one enemy. Barnardo Batiz-Lazo, author of *Cash Box: The Invention and Globalization of the ATM*, says, 'Never before had electronic equipment been so exposed to the elements. The necessity of human intervention in early systems invited further automation. For instance, they could easily jam or run out of product. They could erroneously dispense several bank notes instead of just one – all without the owner's knowledge'.

As banks across the world scrambled to imitate the technology of the early adopters, there were varying levels of success. Several banks operated a token system. 'Some banks would keep the token in the machine and return it to the customer (by post) once the account had been debited,' according to Batiz-Lazo. Eventually, Wetzel's little plastic ATM card was recognised as the solution to most of the teething problems. But it was IBM who played a central role in developing real time networking, enabling the machines to communicate with a bank's computer system and debit customers' accounts instantly.

Although Ulster Bank had introduced a few ATMs in to Ireland already, Bank of Ireland were the first to roll out the system on a widespread basis. They opened their first ATM on February 13th, 1980. It dispensed between £5 and £50 in cash and required customers to have a 'Pass' (Personal Automatic Self Service) card. The *Irish Examiner* heralded the arrival of the device with its headline, 'The 24-hour bank!' and even included a photograph of the 'magic card' that gave you access to the machine.

THE WORLD'S FIRST COMMERCIAL BARBECUE, WEBER, 19

THE BARBECUE

rish writer and surveyor Isaac Weld, visiting the state of Virginia in the mid-1790s, described a peculiar outdoor form of cooking so unusual it merited a paragraph in his celebrated travelogue. 'The people of this part of the country are extremely fond of an entertainment which they call a barbacue. It consists of a large party meeting together, either under some trees or in a house, to partake of a sturgeon or pig roasted in the open air, on a sort of hurdle over a slow fire. This, however, is an entertainment chiefly confined to the lower ranks and, like most others of the same nature, it generally ends in intoxication.'

In December 1492, Christopher Columbus landed on the island we know today as Haiti. In the traditional arrogance of many colonialists, he called it Hispaniola ('Little Spain'). His crew were tired of their rations of biscuit and salt cod and were entranced by the cooking technique of the native Taino people. They smoked fish and iguanas on a wooden rack resting on posts made with sticks, high above a fire pit. This method of smoking food was called *barabicu* which means 'sacred fire pit'.

The Spanish described it as *barbacoa*. However, the Spanish used the word barbacoa not just to describe the wooden rack over a fire, but they also found this new word to be a useful way to describe any sort of raised platform they encountered in the Caribbean. A barbacoa could be a table or even a raised platform for sleeping. When the word was eventually anglicised to 'barbecue', its meaning became uniquely focused on the cooking method. 'The English simply did not need a new word for a raised platform ... As the word came off the tongues of thousands of explorers and settlers, its meaning changed, leaving

SOUTHERN BARBECUE, ENGRAVING BY HORACE BRADLEY, 1887

behind the raised platform and developing a permanent connection to cooking,'
explains Tim Miller in *Barbecue: A History*.

The first English colonists settled in Virginia in 1607. 'The colonists had
come from southern and western England, where roasting was the predominant
cooking technique,' says Miller. 'It was a short jump from roasting a piece of meat
to roasting a whole hog over a fire. Barbecue fit the rough-and-ready lifestyle
of the Southern colonists.' They had brought pigs with them on the ships from
England. These animals were allowed to roam freely in forests and quickly their
numbers multiplied, providing an easy and cheap source of meat for barbecuing.
To this day the cuisine of the Deep South remains proudly associated with this
form of cooking.

George Washington was a big fan of 'barbicues', as he described them in his
diaries. When General Charles Cornwallis surrendered to Washington's rebels
in 1781, people celebrated with barbecues across the country. The tradition
continues to this day with the annual fourth of July 'cookout'. Barbecues were very

much associated with large, outdoor parties involving plenty of liquor and even sideshows such as cockfighting.

By the nineteenth century, barbecues had come to play such an important role in American life that they would be used by politicians as a canvassing tool, a way of gathering people together in one place, with the festivities belying a political agenda. 'The evolution of the political barbecue in the 1830s paralleled the rise of the organized political party system in the United States,' writes Robert F. Moss in *Barbecue: The History of an American Institution*. 'The barbecue was now a serious part of the public discourse over ideas and issues.'

Miller quotes a fascinating description from the *Boston Post* in 1851 of a barbecue in Georgia to celebrate a retiring congressman: 'A trench was dug about 120 feet long, 5 feet wide, and 1 ½ feet deep. Alongside of the trench, piles of wood were burning, and the coals were thrown into the trench, forty hogs and fifteen sheep were spitted and roasting'.

The cooking process at this time would either have employed a spit, as in the previous description, or else a large metal grid would have been placed over the fire trench for grilling. The culinary purpose of barbecue was to slow cook meat to make it as juicy and tender as possible. After the Civil War, former slaves recalled the long hours they would spend over a slow barbecue, basting the meat all through the night before their masters enjoyed the feast the following day.

It wasn't until the twentieth century that barbecuing became a smaller affair, which families could enjoy by themselves. The gradual suburbanisation of America's cities and an emerging middle class contributed to the 'backyard barbecue' phenomenon. This eventually gave rise to a thriving barbecue industry. Henry Ford took advantage of this in the 1920s when he identified a new way of using up the vast amount of wood scraps left over in his Model T factory. Everything from the steering wheels to the dashboards and wheel spokes of his cars were made of wood, but there was a surplus which he wanted to utilise in some way. 'Wood scraps were chipped into small pieces, burned to charcoal, ground into powder, mixed with a binder, and compressed into pillow shaped briquettes,' explains Steven Raichlen in *BBQ USA*. Ford's briquette business would eventually become Kingsford, one of America's largest barbecue charcoal manufacturers to this day.

BARBECUE IN VIRGINIA, 1956

Until the mid-twentieth century, people generally built their own brick or brazier grills in their back gardens. This changed in 1952, when Illinois native George Stephen invented the world's first commercial barbecue. Stephen was a 'backyard barbecuer' but wanted to develop a grill that was resistant to wind and rain and could contain smoke more efficiently. He told the *New York Time* years later in 1977 that barbecuing was a messy business before he came up with his grilling solution. 'I was smoking up the neighborhood and burning up half of what I cooked. What was worse, I had to spend all my time away from the bar, standing there with a squirt gun to put out the fire when the grease hit the hot coals.'

Stephen worked for Weber Brothers Metal Works making nautical buoys and wondered if the kettle design of the buoys could be adapted as a barbecue. Cutting a buoy in half, he put it on three legs and attached a metal grill on top. The other half of the buoy acted as a lid. He inserted air vents in to allow the user to control the temperature and named it the Weber Kettle Grill. It became colloquially known as 'the Sputnik' later in the decade, due to its resemblance to the Soviet satellite. It cost $29.95 (about $285 in today's money).

By 1959 he was selling just 15,000 units a year. People simply didn't see enough reason to buy a barbecue when they could build their own makeshift grill themselves. Stephen and his colleagues began demonstrating their wonder product at malls and supermarkets and soon sales started to sky rocket. By the mid-1970s, half a million Weber Kettles were selling per year. The home barbecue was now firmly established and the phenomenon would soon spread to other parts of the world.

THOR ELECTRIC WASHING MACHINE, 1934. MUSEUM OF SCIENCE AND INDUSTRY, LONDON

THE WASHING MACHINE

A 1921 newspaper advertisement in the United States proclaimed, 'Only a woman knows the joy of an easy washing ... and only a woman knows how much more freedom the THOR ELECTRIC WASHING MACHINE gives her every week'. This invention did exactly that. At a time when housework was strictly gendered, it changed the lives of women around the world by liberating them from the laborious and time-consuming work of cleaning laundry by hand.

The relatively modern notion of washing your underpants after a single use would have been laughed at in the Middle Ages. Not until a separate ecosystem started to grow in your undies did you deem it necessary to give them a rinse in some soapy water. A single set of drawers could get several weeks or even months of use before being washed. People were smelly, but when everyone is smelly then it's a level playing field and everyone just gets on with things as best they can in their own smelly little world.

Two of the major predecessors to the washing machine were the washboard and the washing dolly. The washboard is thought to have originated in Scandinavia in the late eighteenth century and then to have spread throughout Europe. It consisted of a series of wooden grooves against which clothes were vigorously rubbed in order to agitate the dirt. The washing dolly was a T-shaped wooden pole with three or more legs at the opposite end, much like a stool. In her book *English Laundresses: A Social History 1850 - 1930*, Patricia Malcomson describes how it operated: 'The dolly is plunged into the mass and worked by the dollier with both hands with a curious lateral motion to left and right alternately'. This rigorous disturbance of the laundry helped to remove dirt and grime before rinsing.

One of the most important contributions to the rise in laundry was William Gladstone's repeal of the tax on soap in 1853. Prior to this, soap tax is believed to have brought in as much revenue for the exchequer as the levy on alcohol. Campaigners saw it as a tax on the poor because it was measured not by value but by weight. This meant that cheaper soap products, used by the working classes, had the same amount of duty slapped on them as better quality products. This was seen as unfair. It had also led to the inevitable development of soap smuggling and an entire black market in detergent. The new affordability of soap meant that clothing could be washed, not just by the wealthier classes, but by ordinary working families too. It was a hygiene revolution.

However, we must turn to the United States for the technological innovations in washing in the second half of the nineteenth century. While much of Europe remained tied to the shackles of the class system in which the rich outsourced their laundry needs to bevvies of servants, in the US there was a burgeoning middle class with a desire for domestic appliances to make their lives easier.

American inventor James King introduced an idea in 1851 which to this day still makes up a central part of a washing machine. Using a hand crank, the user rotated a perforated metal drum in a tub of soapy water to agitate the fabrics. A very similar device, called Bradford's Patent Washing Machine, was introduced to Ireland in the mid-nineteenth century, this time with an octagonal drum and a mangle attachment. An advertisement in the *Irish Times* in 1860 describes it as 'the most compact Washing, Wringing and Mangling machine that has yet been introduced, the whole process only occupying a few minutes, and doing its work in a very satisfactory manner'. The mangle rolled excess water out of the laundry after washing. There was great variety in these early hand-operated devices. The 'Faithful' washing machine, for example, was a wooden cradle which was designed to be rocked back and forth, thereby encouraging the water and laundry to clash and break down the dirt.

There remains some confusion as to the inventor of the very first electric washing machine, but the Hurley Electric Laundry Equipment Company in Chicago is cited as the first to mass produce an electric product of this type in 1907. This was the Thor, whose landmark advert I mentioned at the beginning of the chapter. It is safe to say that there is little similarity in appearance between the Thor and a modern washer, but it represented a huge step forward.

Historian Lee Maxwell writes in *Save Women's Lives: History of Washing Machines*, 'The first Thor washing machine consisted of a drum type agitation system, a Westinghouse electric motor and a gearing system which enabled the drum, containing the clothes, to be driven eight revolutions in one direction

EARLY TWENTIETH CENTURY WOODEN
WASHING MACHINE WITH MANGLE.

before being automatically reversed and made to rotate the other way'. The electric motor powered a driving belt. This was connected to three separate wheels on the outside of the machine which rotated the drum itself.

Another crucial step forward was the addition of blades into the interior of the drum. This had the effect of lifting the clothes as the drum rotated, ensuring that the laundry didn't bunch together into a wet wad. Have a peek into your washer at home and you'll see this legacy remains to this day. The Thor sat on casters, which was the norm for several decades of the electric washing machine. This allowed the device to be wheeled into the kitchen for the weekly wash. The excess water from the mangle could then be used to wash the floors. Waste not, want not.

We take the spin cycle for granted nowadays, but in the case of early electric washers the laundry came out of its cycle sopping wet. This is where the mangle came in handy. The Thor was fitted with a complicated series of three motorised mangles on top of the drum. The laundry would be fed into the mangle's rollers

to wring the clothes of excess water before being hung up to dry on a line or a clothes horse. The entire machine looks terrifying to modern eyes because there are unencased cogs, belts and levers moving in every direction and you can only imagine how dangerous it could have been if children got near it. The mangle too was infamous for swallowing not just clothes, but fingers as well. In fact, mangled fingers were so common that Leeds Infirmary held a 'mangle clinic' every Thursday morning for a period. The introduction of centrifugal force to spin the clothes at a very high speed eventually made the mangle redundant. And fingers safer.

◄ MANGLE FOR WASHING MACHINE, COMMON BEFORE THE INTRODUCTION OF THE SPIN CYCLE

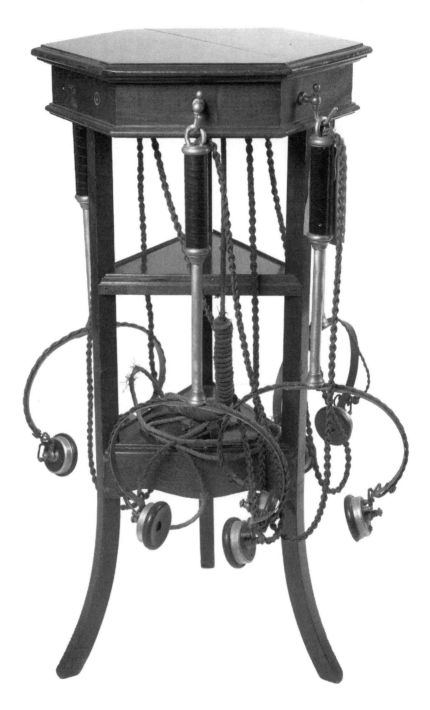

▲ ELECTROPHONE WITH HEADPHONES. LATE NINETEENTH/EARLY TWENTIETH CENTURY.
MUSEUM OF LONDON

HeaDPHones

'The Queen will to-day, for the first time, use the "Electrophone" and hear at Windsor Castle the National Anthem ... given at Her Majesty's Theatre,' proclaimed an article in the *St. James's Gazette* in May, 1899. 'Her Majesty, with the Royal party assembled at the castle, nearly twenty-five miles away, will, by means of the "Electrophone", listen to the boys' hymn as it is sung.'

In 1894, Mr. H.S.J. Booth established the Electrophone Company, transmitting concerts and church services to paid subscribers across London. This was a precursor to radio, allowing customers to dial in from their home telephone and avail of a variety of entertainments. The live events were listened to using headphones, one of the earliest uses of such a device. Each subscriber received two sets to ensure it remained a social activity. The headphone was a large apparatus, more akin to a stethoscope than what we are used to today. The semicircular wire band holding the two headphones together went under the chin so the user was required to hold a long metal rod, with a wooden handle, to keep the apparatus in place.

The company signed deals with a number of theatres, including the Royal Opera House, which allowed them to broadcast live into people's homes. Each of the theatres involved in the service had a row of microphones installed at the front of the stage near the footlights. This was wired back to Electrophone's headquarters in nearby Soho and then broadcast out to homes through the National Telephone Service. Eventually, the network was extended to hospitals across the capital, delivering church services to the sick, with microphones hidden in bibles as priests spoke their homilies. This allowed patients to worship from their beds by simply throwing on a pair of headphones. 'The instruments were connected with various places of worship, and both morning and evening services were successfully carried over the magic wires to the listening invalids,' according to one contemporary newspaper report.

However, this was an expensive service. It cost £5 per annum (£640 in today's money) and was therefore the preserve of the wealthy. The London correspondent of the *Irish Times* reported on his experience of the Electrophone in June 1896. He described it as 'startling' and was astonished that the production of *Hamlet* that he was listening to on 'pairs' (this is how he described headphones) was actually being performed so far away from him, even if it did have a 'far off' effect.

In the 1920s the radio took over, rendering the electrophone redundant. But headphones survived. 'Although there had been trials in which the radio set had been combined with horns to amplify the volume, the headphones continued to be the main form of listening to the radio. It was not until the late 1920s that the loudspeaker became a primary part of the talking machines,' explains Daniel Morat in *Sounds of Modern History*.

The earliest set of headphones had in fact been invented by a French physicist by the name of Ernest Mercadier, in 1891. His 'telephone receivers' (the term 'headphone' had not yet been coined) were designed to free up the hands of telephone operators. But Mercadier's vision was deeper than that. He wanted to create an apparatus which closed 'the ear to external sound,' according to his patent. This late nineteenth century idea of isolating the user from ambient sounds is something which headphone manufacturers have been refining for over a century. His headphones were so advanced that they were more similar to modern earbuds than traditional headphone cans. Each earpiece featured a rubber covering 'to lessen the friction against the orifice of the ear'.

Utah native Nathaniel Baldwin was the first to create the modern headphone when he produced his 'headband for telephone receivers' in 1910. Unlike Mercadier's apparatus, this was actually a *head*phone in that it featured a leather-covered wire which attached to the head itself. 'Within each earphone was, according to legend, a mile of coiled copper wiring and a mica diaphragm to register the wire's signals with vibrations,' as reported by the *New York Times*. He sent his idea to the US Navy who saw great potential in his product for military radio and telephone operators. They started ordering them in bulk, but he couldn't keep up with demand because he could only produce a limited amount from his kitchen workshop in Utah. They asked him to open a factory on the east coast but he refused because as a fundamentalist Mormon and a great supporter of the polygamist movement, he didn't want to leave his community. However, he eventually set up the Baldwin Radio Company and started manufacturing his headphones from a factory in Salt Lake City. By the early 1920s his company was a million-dollar business, producing headphones for a global market.

Up to the mid-twentieth century, headphones were only used by telephone operators or the military. American entrepreneur John Koss saw the potential

TELEPHONE OPERATORS

of headphones as a way of listening to music. He had listened to a song using military grade headphones and described the experience as 'absolutely thrilling'. With the help of his engineer Martin Lange, Koss set about developing an entire home-music system with a phonograph and some headphones he rigged up using 'two vacuum-formed brown plastic cups containing three-inch speakers, protected by a perforated, light plastic cover and foam ear pads,' according to Jimmy Stamp, writing for the *Smithsonian*. 'These were connected by a bent metal rod and the Koss SP-3 headphones were born.'

Users could still listen through a loudspeaker if they wished, but the system also had a 'privacy switch' which meant that the listener could plug in their headphones and listen quietly, without disturbing others. Each phone received different signals, creating a stereophonic experience for the user. Koss demonstrated his headphone system at an audio show in Milwaukee in 1958. It had instant appeal for the new rock 'n roll generation. In *Decoding Dylan*, author Jim Curtis argues that Koss's innovation had a profound impact on the way people experienced music. 'Throughout human history until 1958, people who were listening to music had at least some awareness that a certain distance separated them from the performers of that music. Stereo headphones, however, abolished that distance for the first time.'

◄ SONY WALKMAN

The launch of the Sony Walkman in 1979 changed the way engineers designed headphones. Because this was a portable music system it required very light headphones. Sony moved away from the bulky cup style headphones of the past towards much smaller, neater cushions. In his history of Sony, John Nathan quotes one of the developers of the Walkman, Kozo Ohsone: 'We were all skeptical ... because, at the time in Japan, anything you put in your ears to hear with, including headphones, was associated with impaired hearing, and deafness was a taboo subject. Even the word had been disallowed for use in newspapers and magazines,' he recalled.

So, the company decided to be bold in their advertising and tried to create a new fashion for headphones. An early ad in Japan featured a stylish young woman wearing the ultralight 39 gram headphones while a Buddhist monk, wearing the large and clunky headphones of old, looks disgruntled in the background. Soon, headphones had transcended the functional and become a must-have accessory, fueled by the influence of pop culture icons. Kevin Bacon wore them in the poster for *Footloose* in 1984. Michael J. Fox strapped them around his neck in *Back to the Future* in 1985, while Simon Le Bon sported them in Duran Duran's *A View to a Kill* video.

Sony was also concerned by the isolating nature of the Walkman so the first version featured two headphone jacks, allowing friends to listen together. After a slow beginning, two hundred million Sony Walkmans were eventually sold around the world, crystallizing the preeminence of headphones over loudspeakers for music consumption in the future.

THE HIGH-HEELED SHOE

During the classic 1992 thriller *Single White Female,* the protagonist, played with great relish by Jennifer Jason Lee, is provoked one step too far and stabs a man to death with a five-inch stiletto. This particular style of shoe, a curious symbol of female sexual power, was made possible by the use of steel to create a high-tensile, yet improbably narrow, dagger-like heel.

In 2011 a woman from Augusta, Georgia, named Thelma Carter, was convicted of manslaughter after striking her boyfriend in the head with a stiletto. In 2014, Texas native Ana Trujilo was sentenced to life in prison after bludgeoning her partner to death twenty-five times. Her weapon of choice? A 14cm-high, blue suede, closed-toe stiletto.

When the French fashion designer Andre Perugia designed the world's first stiletto in 1951, the Needle Heel, he was borrowing from the playbook of architects. If a skyscraper could be extremely tall and narrow, so could a shoe. Little did he know that it would eventually be weaponised. After all, the word stiletto means 'little knife' in Italian.

Today we associate high heels with women's fashion. Yet, for much of their history they were the preserve of men and were considered the height of masculinity. A macho man of nobility in seventeenth century Paris wouldn't have dreamed of asking a courtesan to dance without sporting his prettiest high heels and long puffy periwig. The high-heeled shoe, perhaps more than any other

STUFF THAT CHANGED
THE WORLD

form of apparel, shows how definitions of masculinity are in a constant state of evolution.

But where did the high heel originate? Towards the end of the sixteenth century, the Persian army was the largest and most sophisticated in the world. Their cavalry, in particular, was the envy of the world. But if you hopped in a time machine and travelled back to observe the cavalry in action, you would see these virile fighters wearing green leather high-heeled shoes. In an interview with the BBC, Elizabeth Semmelhack of the Bata Shoe Museum, said, 'When the soldier stood up in his stirrups, the heel helped him to secure his stance so that he could shoot his bow and arrow more effectively'.

The Persian leader Shah Abbas I decided to launch a diplomatic extravaganza on the European seats of power in order to bolster greater understanding. The missions he sent to the courts of Russia, Spain and Germany brought this fashion idiosyncrasy with them. Suddenly the European elite began to emulate the Persians and the high-heeled shoe came to represent both nobility and masculinity.

Two particular paintings of a similar period give us an insight into the power of the high heel at this time. In John Michael Wright's wonderfully extravagant portrait of Charles II, dating from the 1660s, the smugness and flamboyance of the restored monarchy is not the only thing on display. Look closely and you will notice the king's shoes, of white leather, a red-painted high heel and a pretty bow to top off the look. Less than four decades later, Louis XIV was painted with almost identical high heels by the French baroque artist Hyacinthe Rigaud. In fact, Louis was so fond of his *talons rouge* that he eventually banned anyone from wearing them apart from himself.

But the big question remains: when did women appropriate the high heel? Perhaps the most important (and bizarre) predecessor to the high heel for women was the *chopine*, an invention of sixteenth century Venice. 'Chopines placed women's feet on platforms that frequently rose to heights of 30 inches or more,' writes Linda O'Keefe in her history of shoes. 'Made of cork or wood, the platforms themselves were usually upholstered in leather of jeweled velvet to match the shoes they supported.'

Like mini stilts, the chopines allowed Venetian noblewomen to take to the

SEVENTEENTH CENTURY CHOPINES. © VICTORIA AND ALBERT MUSEUM, LONDON

streets of the Floating City without the hems of their dresses getting sullied by the filth of the common people below. The platforms were so ludicrously tall and impractical that wearers had to be accompanied by two servants to stop them falling head first into the nearest canal. In fact, so many women were falling over because of their chopines that people began to suspect they were the root cause of a new spate of miscarriages. Because of this, city authorities eventually decreed that chopines had to have an upper limit of 3 inches and no more.

A women's fashion for masculine clothing took place in the mid-seventeenth century in parts of Europe. Adopting the heel was part of this process. A slimmer, more feminine heel replaced the stocky, blockier male heel. Heels had been used by figures such as Louis XIV to represent their natural superiority, but in the period of the Enlightenment the need to display one's credentials became less important. 'Fashion was redefined as frivolous and feminine, and the high heel became a potent accessory of ditsy desirability,' writes Semmelhack in the *New York Times*. In fact, Napoleon had banned the 'Louis heel' as it represented inequality, while Marie Antoinette famously wore two-inch heels as she

EARLY TWENTIETH CENTURY POSTCARD BY JEAN ANGÉLOU

walked up the steps of the guillotine. From this point, on the high heel became principally the domain of women's wear.

The erotic nature of high heels developed in the late nineteenth century and early twentieth centuries when they were adopted in pornography. Just as it has done with many innovations in technology over the years, the pornography industry was very quick to embrace the potential of photographs for their own needs, producing bawdy postcards of women posing in their heels and little else. The postcards were largely made in Paris by photographers such as Jean Agélou and were called 'French postcards' as a result. Despite being made as postcards they were never intended to be sent via the mail, but rather kept as naughty collectibles.

The high-heeled shoe today represents an extraordinary blend of its intricate and diverse history. It can be sophisticated, erotic or simply a practical way of adding a few inches of height. They can also be a wearer's most prized possession. In one particular episode of HBO's *Sex and the City*, Carrie Bradshaw is overwhelmed with grief when a thug steals her heels as a gun is pointed at her head. 'Your watch and your ring, quick!' exclaims the thief, before adding, 'And your Manolo Blahniks!'

1950 ELECTROLUX DISHWASHER. MUSEUM OF SCIENCE AND INDUSTRY, LONDON

26
THE
DISHWASHER

'The woman who succeeds in giving the servant any pride in dishwashing will achieve a great triumph,' advises Molly Bawn on the Women's Page of the *Irish Times* in 1906. In her column, Bawn attempts to offer some helpful tips to readers on how to train the help. 'The servant should be taught to scrape all dishes free from scraps, not with a scratching knife but with a broken piece of crust of bread.' The writer continues at length on the various stages of washing up, the different water temperatures to be used at different stages and the complicated concoction of substances used to help clean all of it. Perhaps surprisingly, the dishwasher was not necessarily invented as a labour-saving device, but rather as a means to wash crockery gently, without the human tendency to break and scrape expensive plates.

Josephine Cochrane, an inventor from Illinois, patented the Garis-Cochrane Dish Washing Machine in 1886, the world's first successful automatic dishwasher. Her husband William had been a dry goods merchant and politician in the Democratic party. They had enjoyed a very comfortable life, with a large home and servants. However, Cochrane was continuously frustrated by her servants chipping and damaging her crockery when they were washing up. When her husband died from alcoholism, leaving her in enormous debt, she decided that finding a mechanical solution to the problem of dishwashing may well be her saving grace.

Within the stamp:

Josephine Cochrane (1839-1913)

Prima mașină de spălat vase

A.D. 1908

ROMÂNIA

3,30 L

2013   Răzvan POPESCU

ROMANIAN STAMP COMMEMORATING JOSEPHINE COCHRANE'S DISHWASHER

In a shed in the back of her garden, Cochrane, with the help of a local mechanic called George Butters, developed a prototype. Cochrane was not the first to develop a dishwashing machine. In 1850 a man by the name of Joel Houghton had patented a machine 'for washing table furniture'. It was essentially a wooden tub with a hand crank which inexpertly splashed water onto a pile of dirty dishes. It wasn't a success, to say the least.

Cochrane, on the other hand, was determined to be methodical in her design. She measured wire compartments to hold plates, cups and saucers firmly in place during the washing process. There was even a special rack for holding cutlery. The wire compartments were placed inside a wheel which sat at the bottom of a copper boiler. The wheel could be turned using a hand crank or by a small motor attached to a pulley system, while hot soapy water was squirted over the dishes. This was the essential genius of her invention. She realised that the exertion of water pressure had the potential to clean dishes more efficiently than scrubbing ever could.

Like so many women inventors at the turn of the century, Cochrane faced many more obstacles then her male counterparts. She recalled later in life, 'I couldn't get men to do the things I wanted in my way until they had tried and failed in their own. And that was costly for me. They knew I knew nothing, academically, about mechanics, and they insisted on having their own way with my invention until they convinced themselves my way was the better, no matter how I had arrived at it'. She presented her unique operating system at the World's Columbian Exposition in Chicago in 1893 and won the top prize for 'Best Mechanical Construction.'

Hotels were the first establishments to show an interest in Cochrane's invention. An automated method of dealing with copious amounts of dirty dishes was an intriguing prospect.

One day she found herself in the lobby of the Shermann House Hotel in Chicago, touting for business. She later recalled to a journalist, 'You asked me what was the hardest part of getting into business … I think, crossing the great lobby of the Sherman House alone. You cannot imagine what it was like in those days … for a woman to cross a hotel lobby alone. I had never been anywhere without my husband or father – the lobby seemed a mile wide. I thought I should faint at every step, but I didn't – and I got an $800 order as my reward'.

But hospitals and colleges took an interest too. Soon she had enough orders to start her own company, the Garis-Cochran Manufacturing Company, which operated its factory from an abandoned school.

A 1909 advertisement for her machine shows a device which is almost unrecognisable to modern eyes. It is an enormous cylindrical metal tank on four legs which opens at the front like a giant steel mouth. Inside are trays of crockery with water pipes and jets in every direction. It looks industrial, unwieldy and cumbersome. The copy reads, 'You can have absolutely clean dishes, and have them quick, without being nicked, cracked or broken by using the new improved Garis-Cochrane Dish Washing Machine.'

In 1914 her company reimagined her dishwashing device as a much smaller, more compact machine for home use. It didn't sell. The company was perplexed and went about doing a survey of housewives to discover why a labour-saving device such as this wasn't welcome in the American home. The results were very telling. It revealed that housewives' least favourite job was washing laundry. However, 'the majority of women questioned in 1915 reported that doing dinner dishes was a welcome relaxer at the end of a hard day,' says historian Charles Panati.

There were other reasons why the dishwasher wouldn't take off in the home at that time. The lack of sufficient volumes of hot water meant that dishes often came out grubby. Housewives still believed that hard graft and elbow grease was the best method of cleaning dishes. At a cost of $150 (about $4,500 in today's money), the machine remained prohibitively expensive for most consumers. But Cochrane's company survived, eventually becoming KitchenAid, a division of the home appliance giant Whirlpool.

In 1929, the German businessman and innovator Carl Miele introduced the first electric dishwasher to Europe. It was a white top-loading tub on three casters and cost three times the annual salary of a housekeeper at the time. Its launch coincided with the Wall Street Crash. For both these reasons his product was not a priority for consumers.

The British engineer William Howard Livens introduced essential changes to the dishwasher in the mid-twentieth century, making the machine what it is today. Livens' journey to dishwasher pioneer was an unlikely one. During World War One he was responsible for inventing a successful projectile for the delivery of poisonous gas. After the Germans used gas as a weapon for the first time in the Battle of Ypres in 1915, the British realised that they needed to develop better technology in this area. The Livens Projector could deliver 30 pounds of

KENWOOD DISHWASHER, 1952.
MUSEUM OF SCIENCE AND INDUSTRY,
LONDON

poisonous phosphene gas at the enemy and continued in use until World War Two. Between the wars, Livens found time to improve dishwasher technology. In 1924 he built a machine which contains many features we would recognise in a modern dishwasher: a front loading washer with a rotating sprayer. He also introduced a heating element in 1940 which dried the crockery, sparing users the tedium of hand drying the dishes once they were washed.

The post-war period finally saw the realisation of the dishwasher as a viable home appliance. As more and more homes had access to quantities of hot water and electricity, the dishwasher slowly caught on. Molly Bawn wouldn't have believed her eyes if she had seen an advertisement for the Thor Automagic in her own newspaper, the *Irish Times*, in May 1951. 'Without your hands touching water, the Thor washes, rinses and dries clothes – does the dishes too!' Thor had launched this incredible product back in the mid-1940s. Almost unbelievably, to our modern understanding of home appliances, the Automagic had interchangeable interior tubs: one for laundry and another for crockery. It didn't last long on the market. Thor soon realised that consumers were squeamish about washing their dirty undies in the same place as the bowl they used for eating their breakfast.

ANCIENT ROMAN TOILETS AT OSTIA, ANTICA

THE TOILET

In 2017 I found myself in a little village called Houay Xai, along the Mekong river in Laos. This sleepy little village is on the edge of the jungles of Bokeo province. In the bathroom in my hostel there was a little sign which had a picture of a man squatting on a toilet. But his feet were actually *on* the toilet seat as he hovered over the bowl. There was a red line crossed through the image, indicating that this was forbidden. At first I was perplexed by the sign. Why on earth would someone climb up onto the toilet and stand on it when there was a seat built into it? Afterwards, I realised that the Western flush toilet was something that was relatively new to this part of the world, where squat holes had been the norm. These signs offered guidance on how to use the new technology correctly.

In another adventure I stayed in a *casa particular* in Havana one night and was told that I couldn't put any toilet paper in the toilet bowl. All paper had to be put in a bin provided – a less than ideal situation in the sweltering Cuban summer. The country's plumbing and sewerage system simply couldn't handle toilet paper. These issues give us an insight into the evolution of the toilet, and how sanitation systems continue to develop in different societies around the world.

The Romans were among the earliest civilisations to introduce working latrine systems. In her book *How the Toilet Changed History,* Laura Perdew writes that by the fourth century AD there were some 143 communal latrines in the city of Rome, flushed by the brilliant engineering of the aqueducts into the Cloaka Maxima sewer system. Going to the toilet in Ancient Rome was often a sociable, even convivial, activity. Nowadays, urinals are about as public as going to the toilet gets, but in earlier times even doing a poo was done side by side, as you chatted away with your fellow defecators. The sweating, panting, plops and odours were shared in a completely open space.

In Ostia Antica, just west of Rome, some of the city's ancient latrines can still be seen to this day. One particular latrine consists of a large room, lined on each side with long stone benches. Each bench is punctuated with several horseshoe shaped holes which users sat over, in full view of each other. Business could be discussed while at the same time attending to the call of nature. In front of the bench ran a small channel of water. A number of communal sponges on sticks were provided to the patrons. These would be dipped in the channel of water and used to wipe the posterior, before being left back in the salt water drain for the next user. This all seems rather nasty and unhygienic to our modern sensitivities, but the provision of public toilets was a momentous step forward from squatting in the street like a dog.

Typically of the Ancient Romans, even the toilets were artfully created. A latrine in Pompeii features a fresco of Fortuna, the goddess of luck, who is invoked to protect patrons' bottoms from the rats in the sewer below or, more catastrophically, the build-up of combustible methane gas.

The medieval garderobe was an important milestone in the evolution of the toilet. The word derives from the French, *garder* meaning to keep, *robe* meaning clothes, as people would keep their wardrobe in this room. The pungent smells from the privy were thought to deter moths from the fabrics, and presumably infuse one's clothes with the heady aroma of urine. An alternative origin story for *eau de toilette*? A chute ran from the holes and carried waste outside the walls of the castle or into a moat or area of ground away from the entrance, as seen in the garderobe at Peveril Castle in Derbyshire.

The garderobe in Barryscourt Castle, a sixteenth century tower house in Co. Cork, offers a revealing insight into how these rooms functioned. It features a stone bench covered with a long board with two holes. This allowed two people to use the facility at the same time. Like the Romans, embarrassment and privacy issues were not yet associated with a trip to the toilet, apparently.

▲ THE GARDEROBE AT PEVERIL CASTLE, CASTLETON, DERBYSHIRE, ENGLAND

In *Daily Life in the Middle Ages*, author Paul B. Newman notes that 'the financial accounts for many noble households (in England) reveal routine payments to *gongfermers*, men who made their living by digging out and carting away the solid waste that accumulated in these pits and ditches'. It is believed that the windows in garderobes were often left without glass in order to prevent the build up of noxious fumes from the chute. One can only imagine how chilly it was to pull down one's pyjamas for a quick pee on a frosty winter's morning.

During the medieval period we see the rise in euphemistic language around toilet use. For example, some monasteries had a 'necessarium', a room for monks to retire to when 'necessary' things needed to be done. Indeed, the word 'gong', from the gongfermer, was a slang word for faeces. Privy, with its earliest citation in 1225, according to the *Oxford English Dictionary*, was derived from the French to describe 'a private place'. Henry VIII famously employed a 'Groom of the Stool', a man with a dirty job but with great influence as he was known to have the 'ear of the king'. His job was to look after the intimate hygiene needs of his royal master. He slept at the foot of the king's bed and was on hand at all occasions with a special velvet covered stool, with a round opening, which held a chamber pot underneath. This is where we get the lavatorial meaning of the word stool, which we still use today.

Sir John Harrington, one of the 102 godchildren of the childless Queen Elizabeth I, installed the world's first flush toilet in Richmond Palace in 1596. His contribution to sanitation is believed by many to have led to the slang word 'the john' to describe a toilet. His invention featured an oval bowl sealed with resin and wax. This was connected by a pipe to a cistern on the floor above the toilet itself. It required 28 litres of water per flush. This demanded such a huge effort

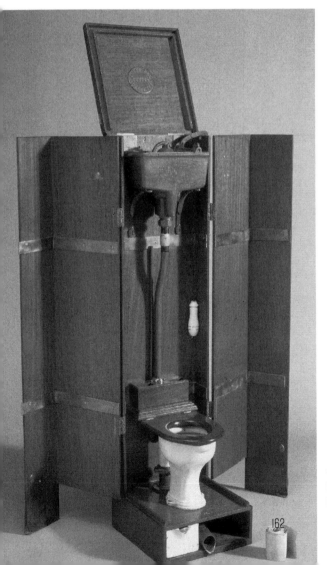

from servants to carry large amounts of water up through the building that Harrington suggested 20 uses of the toilet between flushings. Harrington's invention wasn't a success, for two reasons: firstly, her Majesty didn't like the roar of the flush as she felt it advertised her private ablutions too loudly and, secondly, the flush toilet couldn't truly become a success until the introduction of widespread plumbing.

An Edinburgh watchmaker by the name of Alexander Cummings changed the toilet forever in 1775. The connection

◄ MODEL OF JENNING'S PATENT WATER CLOSET, ENGLAND 1895–1905. SCIENCE MUSEUM, LONDON between plumbing and watch making is not an obvious one, and goodness knows why he got involved in this business, but Cummings made history when he designed the S-trap, which we still benefit from today. Before this invention, toilets were open to the sewer below. His cunning innovation trapped a pool of water in the pipe, thus preventing the entry of putrid gases into the bathroom.

A Brighton plumber by the name of George Jennings built the toilets for the Crystal Palace, site of the Great Exhibition of 1851. He charged one penny to use his 'retiring room', leading to the popular expression 'spend a penny'. Over 800,000 people paid for the privilege during the course of the exhibition, marvelling at the unusual experience of a flushing water closet.

However, refilling the cistern after each use of the toilet remained a problem. Enter, Sir Thomas Crapper! Crapper is often mistakenly described as the inventor of the flush toilet, perhaps because his surname has become synonymous with the activity. But he did introduce a major breakthrough: the floating ballcock. His invention automatically refilled the cistern after each use, made possible of course by the increased availability of plumbing and sewage networks.

Crapper developed a very successful line of toilets and plumbing equipment, eventually receiving a royal warrant. A growing demand for bathroom facilities led him to open the world's first toilet showroom in London in 1870, a bold move in the often prudish atmosphere of the Victorian age. The royal family sealed his reputation when they hired him to install his flushing toilets in Sandringham Castle in the 1880s, proving once and for all that kings and queens do indeed sit on the throne.

▲ HUNTLEY & PALMERS CHRISTMAS BISCUITS

28

THE BISCUIT

The digestive biscuit, as the name suggests, began its life in the early nineteenth century as a remedy for flatulence. While discussing the merits of J. Hutchinson's celebrated Digestive Biscuits in a Manchester newspaper in 1829, the writer claimed that 'these biscuits, when genuine, and taken regularly by families, have the good property of keeping the body in a regular state, and in a great measure supersedes the necessity of having recourse to medicine'. The digestive biscuit would achieve international acclaim in 1892 when Alexander Grant, working for McVitie and Price, introduced bicarbonate of soda to the coarse brown flour recipe. This was believed to aid digestion and settle the tummy.

Nowadays, the term 'biscotti' describes a fancy little biscuit which might accompany a cappuccino in a swanky cafe, yet its trendiness belies two thousand years of history. The biscotti, perhaps the world's first biscuit, has its origins in the second century BC when Romans developed it as a foodstuff which could remain fresh during the long travels of the empire's legionaries. Pliny the Elder claimed that they 'would be edible for centuries'. The word biscuit derives directly from biscotti which means 'twice cooked' in Latin. A dough of flour, eggs and nuts was baked, cut into fingers and then baked again to make them as dry as possible. It was this absence of moisture which made them durable and resilient to spoiling. They were so hard that they would often be dunked in wine to soften while eating.

In fact, the biscuit has a long association with military history. When Richard the Lionheart set off on his crusade to the Holy Land in 1190, his ships were stocked with 'biskit of muslin' made with barley, rye and bean flour. But it was Samuel Pepys, the famous seventeenth century diarist, who secured the biscuit's place in the Royal Navy. Pepys is often considered the father of the modern Royal Navy due to his successful attempts to root out corruption in the service and reorganise ration supplies for sailors. It was Samuel Pepys who first regularised Navy 'victualing' and worked out the first comprehensive table of rations which included 'one pound daily of good, clean, sweet, sound, well-baked and well-conditioned wheaten biscuit (plus a galleon of beer and other victuals)', according to the Royal Museums Greenwich.

The sailors called these biscuits 'hardtack' or 'molar breakers' because they were notoriously difficult to bite into and often broke their teeth. They were also routinely infested with weevils. 'Before each meal, a tapping noise could be heard, which was the men tapping their biscuits against the table to knock the worms out of it,' says Rex Hickox in his history of the Navy. During the American Civil War, soldiers were also issued with hardtack. They would dunk them in coffee, forcing the weevils to the surface. They would then bail them out of their mugs and continue eating. They were often called sea biscuits in the United States, leading to the naming of the famous 1940's racehorse, whose father, incidentally, was named Hardtack.

By the late eighteenth century, the bake house in Plymouth alone was producing 16,000 rations of biscuits per day. For over two centuries the biscuit went some way to solving a perennial problem for seafaring powers: how to provide non-perishable food for their sailors that would remain

BISCOTTI, MEANING
'TWICE COOKED'
ORIGINATED IN
ANCIENT ROME

edible over great distances and long periods of time. Hardtack remained the breakfast of champions until the introduction of canned food to the Royal Navy in 1813.

The eating of biscuits shifted in the early nineteenth century from the military to a snack consumed by everyone. The expansion of travel during this period saw the rise of the biscuit as the ideal travel snack. Joseph Huntley owned a small bakery opposite a posting inn for stage coaches in Reading. He began selling his biscuits to passengers who would eat them on their long journey back to London. When rail travel became common in the second half of the nineteenth century, Huntley &

▲ HARDTACK, 1864

Palmers, as it had become, began supplying first class passengers with a neatly wrapped biscuit for their trip. By 1900 the company was the largest biscuit manufacturer in the world with 5,000 employees and it was exporting all over the world.

Huntley & Palmers' 400 different varieties of biscuit gives us an insight into just how popular this snack had become by the turn of the twentieth century. They introduced airtight tins as a way of making their product last even longer and also as a way to make their biscuits stand out with enticing branding. Tins of 'Long Jamaica,' 'NICE' and 'Ginger Wafers' came in ornate, colourful tins that were fashionable to display to visitors as the phenomenon of afternoon tea took hold. Huntley & Palmers emphasised their international success in their advertising by quoting letters they had received from far flung parts of the globe. One 1904 ad featured an illustration of the Victoria Falls with a letter reading, 'As we were boating on the Zambesi, just above the Falls, one of our boats took in a good deal of water; the native baled out the water with a 'Huntley & Palmers' biscuit tin. It was so unexpected to find such an emblem of civilization in this, the interior of Africa'.

As the biscuit gained in popularity in England, a similar snack called a cookie had taken hold in America. But why do Americans use the word 'cookie'? To find an answer to this we need to travel back to the early seventeenth century when thousands of Dutch immigrants settled in New Amsterdam, a town that would later become known as Manhattan. They brought with them their recipe for 'koekie', which translates as 'small cake'. The popularity of koekie spread and was eventually anglicised to 'cookie'. The Dutch also brought their tradition of Sinterklass to New Amsterdam which the Americans would later adopt as Santa Claus. What an influential bunch.

The chocolate chip cookie, that most American of snacks, came into being in 1930. Ruth Wakefield ran a restaurant called the Toll House Inn in Massachusetts. She was used to making cookies in which the already melted chocolate was mixed into the dough before cooking. One day she decided to experiment and add crumbled chunks of Nestlé chocolate to the dough instead. She had unwittingly created an American classic. They were an instant hit and soon the recipe started appearing in New

◄ CHOCOLATE CHIP COOKIE

England newspapers and was even broadcast by Betty Crocker on her popular radio programme. Nestlé agreed to an arrangement with Wakefield. She would get unlimited amounts of free chocolate for her restaurant and Nestlé could print her recipe on the back of their semi-sweet cooking chocolate. Eventually Nestlé would start manufacturing their own Toll House Chocolate Chip Cookies, sparking an industry which continues to this day.

Cheers up everything —and everybody

It gives flavour to an unpromising steak or chop and *verve* to a promising one. It helps your Monday cold cut recover its Sunday zest and causes your *fish* to take on a new and delicious taste.

Tomatoes fresh from the garden — whole, sound, juicy, sun-ripened—bottled the day they are picked, and in the gardens where they are grown. Seasoned with a rare spice blend. A rich, thick, tangy, appetising sauce. Can you imagine anything more delicious ?

HEINZ TOMATO KETCHUP

29
KETCHUP

When Robert de Niro's character picks up a bottle of Heinz Ketchup in the 1990 crime classic *Goodfellas* I am always tickled by the method he employs to get the sauce out of the bottle. This is a problem which tormented me as a child. I loved ketchup but how could I encourage a reluctant substance out of a glass receptacle? De Niro rolls it vigorously between two flat palms until the condiment eventually slips onto his plate. The actor was so determined to be faithful to the mannerisms of real life gangster Jimmy Conway (AKA 'The Irishman') that he had even researched how he handled a bottle of ketchup. This speaks to the universality of ketchup. It is a food that is so widespread in its appeal and so ubiquitous on kitchen tables that everyone has their own personal relationship with it. It sits quietly at the back of fridges waiting to be rolled, squeezed or squirted onto millions of plates every evening.

For most of its history ketchup had nothing to do with tomatoes whatsoever. Its origins are as a fishy brine to be added to other foods for flavour. Its nineteenth century transformation into a sugary tomato condiment tells us very little about how the story of ketchup began. There are many hypotheses about its beginnings, but the etymological confusion over its spelling makes concrete conclusions difficult.

Although we generally call it ketchup nowadays, for much of its history it was known as 'catchup' or 'catsup.' This confusion was brought brilliantly to light in an 1864 article in the *Irish Times* about mushrooms and their inclusion in

◄ ADVERTISMENT FOR HEINZ TOMATO KETCHUP, DATED 1928

ketchup recipes. The writer discusses the versatility of the mushroom, a vegetable which seemed to be experiencing a moment of great interest at that time, when she mentions, 'we have what is well known to almost everybody, the expressed juice called catsup, katchup or ketchup. This word, which is spelt in various ways, is quite a puzzle to philologists'. The writer continues to ponder the origins of the word, noting that 'some suppose it to be derived from Kuck-hup, a Hindustanese word for turtle'. Although there is little evidence of ketchups made out of turtle meat, there are a number of species of the animal which are native to India, so there may be some truth in this hypothesis.

Another theory is that it has its origins in China where a food called 'kê-tsiap', meaning 'the brine of pickled fish' was used in a dialect of Chinese called Amoy. According to HT Huang, author of *Fermentations and Food Science*, kê-tsiap 'was a favourite condiment among Chinese fishermen in the eighteenth century. To the ears of the Western sailors on the ship (it) sounded very much like ketchup. Thus, ketchup was born'.

Ketchup was essentially a way of preserving foods in the days before refrigeration. One of its main ingredients was brine, which is a mix of salt and water that creates lactic acid. This in turn destroys harmful bacteria. The British brought these ideas back from Asia to Britain where they became popular. The first ever recipe for ketchup, at least in the English language, was in an edition of the *Compleat Housewife* from 1727. To make 'katchop' (a uniform spelling clearly hadn't been agreed on as yet) required 12 to 14 anchovies, ten to twelve shallots, white wine vinegar, ordinary white wine, mace, ginger, cloves, pepper, nutmeg, lemon peel and horseradish.

◄ BROOKS CATSUP BOTTLE WATER TOWER, ILLINOIS, USA

As the eighteenth century wore on, there was a growing craze for all things ketchupy with people testing out a wide variety of different ingredients. Jane Austen, for example, was very partial to walnut ketchup, according to the household book recorded by her friend Martha Lloyd. Another recipe from 1742 called 'Katch-Up that will Last Twenty Years' called for the addition of a gallon of stale beer which would 'give both taste and colour beyond any other ingredients'. Writing in *Pure Ketchup: A History of America's National Condiment*, Andrew F. Smith explains, 'The proliferation of so many diverse ketchup recipes can be attributed to the inventiveness, resourcefulness and British culinary ingenuity during the eighteenth century'.

To gain any understanding of the absence of tomatoes in ketchup before the nineteenth century, we need to tease out the deep unease and distrust people had about this fruit. Writing for the *Smithsonian Magazine*, K. Annabelle Smith says the tomato was known as the 'poison apple' because there was a belief that it caused aristocrats to die. The truth of the matter was that the acid in the tomatoes attracted the lead in the pewter of dinner plates in wealthy homes, which, in turn, caused sickness in those who ate them. But there was something else which made people treat tomatoes with extreme suspicion. Food writer Sara Bir says, 'Tomatoes – *Lycopersicon esculentum* – are in the Solanaceae family, which includes deadly nightshades and other poisonous plants; part of the tomato taboo was guilt by association'.

An American farmer named Robert Gibbon Johnson bucked the trend. He believed tomatoes to be harmless and wanted to change consumer beliefs on the matter. In 1820, in front of a crowd of 2,000 people, he did a live demonstration in which he ate a basket of tomatoes. Presumably the crowd were hoping for a sort of Iron Stomach situation with live and hilarious vomiting. They were to be disappointed. He was perfectly fine after eating the tomatoes. Apparently a doctor had been on standby in case he was poisoned, but Johnson wanted to be living proof of their harmlessness. The Civil War in America also changed the fortunes of the tomato. As a foodstuff they were easily and cheaply canned and provided excellent fodder for the thousands of ravenous Union soldiers.

But even after the distrust of tomatoes had vanished, their addition to ketchup created a plethora of problems. The difficulty lay in the ability to preserve tomatoes over a long period of time. The tomato season lasts from August to

▲ HEINZ KETCHUP BOTTLE, 1882

October in the United States, but consumers wanted ketchup all year around. Manufacturers started adding harmful preservatives such as salicylic acid, benzoate of soda and boric acid to their product in order to supply the enormous demand throughout the year. When the pulp was sieved out of the product they were left with a yellowish substance. Consumers wanted red ketchup, not a yellow mess, so manufacturers began adding coal tar to make it redder in colour. This, of course, was a carcinogenic.

A study was carried out in 1896 to determine the ill effects of commercial ketchups. It found that 90% of ketchup products on the market had 'injurious ingredients'. Something had to change. This is when a pioneering Pittsburg native arrived on the scene. His innovations and legacy would change the ketchup industry forever.

Henry J. Heinz started making ketchup in 1876, inspired by his mother's homemade recipe. Like his competitors, Heinz had used coal tar dye in his products initially, but by the turn of the century he had revolutionised the recipe and made it safe. He cut out the presence of all chemical preservatives and added natural ones instead. Quentin Skrabec, Heinz's biographer, says, 'While ketchup (called catsup at the time) was a very small product offering for Heinz, Noble and Company, the company developed a lot of the necessary manufacturing practices ... his recipe called for more tomato pulp as well as more sugar and vinegar. Roughly twenty to twenty-five tomatoes were needed in a bottle of Heinz catsup.'

In a time when hygiene in factories was questionable to say the least, Heinz set the standard for the future of food manufacturing. According to Skrabec, his factory floors were scrubbed daily. This is something we presume food factories would do nowadays but this level of cleanliness was revolutionary in the late nineteenth century and helped to create a safe ketchup that would last. By 1906 Heinz was producing six million bottles of ketchup per year from half a million bushels of tomatoes, proudly stating on the label that his catsup was 'free from benzoate of soda'.

But we still haven't resolved the etymological debate regarding the spelling of this delicious condiment. When Heinz Tomato Catsup was battling for business during the 1880s they decided to change their brand to Heinz Tomato *Ketchup* as a way to distinguish themselves in a crowded market. Once they became the most popular ketchup brand, their competitors began to convert to the word ketchup too. However, even to this day, pockets of catsup lovers can still be found in certain parts of the United States.

GAS STREET LAMP IN LONDON

THE LAMP POST

In 1909 there were 4,400 gas street lamps in Dublin. These were lit and extinguished every day by a team of Corporation workers in blue uniforms and caps, carrying an oil-lighted rod to ignite their wicks and a set of keys to open and close their glass cases. They operated by burning a gas that was distilled from coal, a process originally pioneered by Scottish engineer William Murdoch. Gas lamps first took over from the weaker and less efficient oil lanterns in the 1820s and lasted until the 1950s when electricity conquered its competitors. 'Some lamplighters, as members of the IRA, played a clandestine role on the streets during the Troubles (The War of Independence),' says historian Kevin Kearns. When the Black and Tans instituted a curfew, the lamplighters were among the few who were offered an exemption. This gave them an ideal cover to hide ammunition and deliver messages after dark.

Gas street lights had been common, even in regional parts of Ireland, since the mid-nineteenth century. An article in the *Kerry Evening Post* in 1860 announced that Tralee was to receive eight new gas lamps for areas of the town which were still insufficiently lit. These lamps needed constant maintenance. The *Post* revealed that 'some of the lamplighters were fined for neglect of duty, particularly in not having the street lamps properly cleaned'. But it could also be dangerous work, with one gaslight exploding in the face of a lamplighter as he was working in Belfast in 1828. This wasn't an isolated incident. The dangers associated with gas lamps and the fear of the gasometers which fed them was ever present. 'Explosions flattened buildings, sent bricks and debris flying, and killed and maimed workers, householders, pedestrians and shoppers in nearby bakeries and butcher shops,' explains Jane Brox in *Brilliant: The Evolution of Artificial Light*.

Many were extremely sceptical about the prospect of artificial light when it was first introduced as an idea. Sir Walter Scott, the author of *Rob Roy*, famously wrote at the time, 'There is an idiot here proposing to light London with – what do you think? – smoke!' People were incredulous at the idea that burning gas could create light. The very first use of gas street lighting took place in Pall Mall in London. It was illuminated for George III's birthday in 1807, drawing crowds of amazed onlookers, marvelling at the miracle of artificial light. However, it wouldn't be until 1812 that the world's first gas company, the Gas Light and Coke Company, came into operation. They established the first permanent gas street lights on Westminster Bridge on December 31st 1813. Gas street lighting made people feel safer on a city's streets and also had the effect of increasing business hours as pedestrians were more willing to roam the city after dark.

The immediate predecessor to systems of public street lighting in London were the linkboys of the seventeenth century. Linkboys were children who carried flaming torches and could be hired for a farthing to negotiate the darkness and filth of the streets and escort a gentleman home safely. 'It was commonly feared that a linkboy, exploiting his client's vulnerability, might blow out his link and cause an offence. They would "knock down gentlemen in Drink, and lead others out of the way into Dark and Remote places"', writes Emily Cockayne in *Hubbub: Filth, Noise & Stench in England 1600-1770*.

But when did public street lighting programmes begin? In 1667 Louis XIV had pioneered a candle light system in Paris. By the early eighteenth century, there were 5,400 candle lanterns in place across the centre of the city, operating from dusk and from October to March only, the darkest months of the year. The lanterns were attached to ropes which were strung across streets between two buildings. To light them they were lowered using a pulley system. The lanterns took on a dark new role in 1789 when the revolutionaries would hang the nobility from them, before the guillotine took over as the grisly punishment of choice.

Amsterdam is considered to be the first city in Europe to introduce a successful and efficient system of oil street lamps. The artist Jan van der Heyden designed a special oil lantern which used the flow of air to clean soot off the glass, thereby solving the perennial problem of blackened lamps. This was also the first instance of positioning a street light on a lamp post, as opposed to being suspended on ropes, as in Paris. Van Heyden's unique design was soon spreading to other cities in Europe, including Berlin and Dublin. His lighting system remained in use in Amsterdam from the late seventeenth century right up to 1840.

Gaslight became king in the nineteenth century. However, it was handicapped by its weak luminosity. Rather than lighting up streets the way we are accustomed to today, they instead offered

▲ DESIGN FOR A STREET LIGHT LANTERN (BETWEEN 1674-1679) BY JAN VAN DER HEYDEN

little pools of light to guide you on your way, made murkier by the dense smog of Victorian industry. Electricity offered a brighter future. In the late nineteenth century, moonlight towers represented early forms of electric street lighting. These enormous towers could reach 230 feet in height. They had multiple electric arc lights attached at the top, which then beamed a powerful wave of illumination down on the city below. While a single gas light offered the equivalent of 16

▲ NINETEENTH CENTURY VIEW OF A MOONLIGHT TOWER IN NEW ORLEANS

candles, moon towers had a candlepower of between 2,000 and 6,000, depending on its size.

Aurora, a small city in Illinois, was the first to get electric street lights in America. Six moon towers were installed, magically bathing the town in glorious, artificial light. The towers worked well in a flat city such as Aurora with wide, open streets. 'The greatest test of the tower system came in Detroit,' argues Ernest Freeberg in *The Age of Edison*. 'Eager to proclaim their city the best lighted in the world, (they built) no fewer than seventy massive light towers, each 150 feet tall.' This was a grand and dangerous experiment as some towers came crashing down and others were vandalised by disgruntled residents. Eventually, the city was immersed in an eerie half light that caused havoc on wildlife. 'In some spots it performed all too well, keeping geese and chickens awake all night until they began to die of exhaustion,' says Freeberg.

By the early twentieth century moonlight towers started to be phased out. While they enjoyed limited success, ultimately they were seen as less than ideal. Trees and tall buildings could block a tower's beam and cast large areas of a city into blackness. The harshness of the blue light coming from the towers startled pedestrians and a consensus grew that smaller, localised street lamps were, after

▲ MOONLIGHT TOWER IN AUSTIN, TEXAS

all, the best way of lighting a city. However, seven moon towers are still lit in the city of Austin in Texas every night to this day, one of them being the site of the famous party scene in Richard Linklater's classic 1993 stoner movie *Dazed & Confused*.

Thomas Edison changed street lighting forever when he invented the incandescent light bulb in the 1870s. The first instance in which his new technology was employed for street lighting was in Holborn in London where 232 incandescent lamp posts were installed in 1882. Edison's revolution in lighting would eventually spread across the world, illuminating urban areas like never before, blurring the ever-decreasing line between night and day.

He's one of the busiest men in town. While his door may say *Office Hours 2 to 4*, he's actually on call 24 hours a day.

The doctor is a scientist, a diplomat, and a friendly sympathetic human being all in one, no matter how long and hard his schedule.

According to a recent Nationwide survey:

MORE DOCTORS SMOKE CAMEL THAN ANY OTHER CIGARETTE

DOCTORS in every branch of medicine—113,597 in all—were queried in this nationwide study of cigarette preference. Three leading research organizations made the survey. The gist of the query was—What cigarette do you smoke, Doctor?

The brand named most was Camel!

The rich, full flavor and cool mildness of Camel's superb blend of costlier tobaccos seem to have the same appeal to the smoking tastes of doctors as to millions of other smokers. If you are a Camel smoker, this preference among doctors will hardly surprise you. If you're not—well, try Camels now.

Your "T-Zone" Will Tell You.

T for Taste . . .
T for Throat

that's your proving ground for any cigarette. See if Camels don't suit your "T-Zone" to a "T"

R. J. Rey.
Tobacco Co.
Winston-Sale

CAMELS *Costlier Tobaccos*

▲ ADVERTISEMENT FOR CAMEL CIGARETTES, 1946

THE CIGARETTE

In the West we see the cigarette as something that is in decline. Smoking rates in Europe, for example, hover between 20% and 30%. But this gives us a misleading understanding of tobacco use on a global scale. For example, Indonesian men are amongst the most extensive smokers in the world, with a 67% prevalence rate and a growth forecast of 5% per year, according to the World Health Organisation. The 'golden age' of tobacco use in Europe and America perhaps reached its giddy zenith when RJ Reynolds ran the 'More doctors smoke Camel than any other cigarette' campaign in 1949, but those days are now long gone, in the West at least.

The cigarette was a seventeenth century invention. Prior to this, tobacco had been smoked in pipes and in cigar form for purposes of ritual in Latin American cultures. It started to be cultivated in modern day Peru and Ecuador between 5000 and 3000 BC. When European colonists, such as Christopher Columbus, arrived in the Caribbean in 1492 they marvelled at this new drug which was employed for its supposed healing properties. 'Chiefs engaged in ritual blowing, in which they would blow smoke at the heads and faces of tribe members,' writes Allan Brandt in *The Cigarette Century*. Columbus himself recorded its use in his journal: '… they chew and suck or take in with their breath that smoke which dulls their flesh and as it were intoxicates and so they say that they do not feel weariness. They call (them) tobacos'.

French diplomat and scholar Jean Nicot is credited with bringing tobacco to the French court in the sixteenth century, where it would become increasingly popular. Because of this, his name would later come to describe the active ingredient in tobacco: nicotine. Like the people of America, Europeans regarded tobacco as a medical marvel. It was prescribed for everything from the common cold to toothaches. It was even claimed that it reduced bad body odour and that it could cure the plague.

The great explorer Sir Walter Raleigh popularised the smoking of tobacco in the court of Elizabeth I. People took readily to Raleigh's smoking, but were far more suspicious about the potato, a new vegetable he had also brought back from his travels. While Raleigh was imprisoned in the Tower of London in 1618, prior to his execution for treason, his tobacco pouch was among his last possessions. The leather wallet, which is now on display in the Wallace Collection in London, bears the insignia *Comes meus fuit in illo miserrimo tempore* (It was my companion at this most miserable time). This suggests that even in the early seventeenth century, people were already becoming addicted to this new drug.

The Mayans had smoked dried and rolled tobacco leaves as primitive cigars. But the paper cigarette, as we know it today, is a European invention, according to Robert Proctor, author of *Golden Holocaust: Origins of the Cigarette Catastrophe*. 'Paper wrapping is one thing that distinguishes the modern fag from its fatter browner brethren, and the fashion seems to have come about by accident, in the first half of the seventeenth century, in Seville in Spain ... where beggars rolled papaletes from tobacco scraps.' Cigarettes therefore began as the lowly cousin of the posh and more expensive cigar – discarded scraps of tobacco rolled in cheap bits of paper. The French christened this new means of smoking as *une cigarette*. This is a diminutive of cigar, derived from the Mayan word *sik'ar*, which means smoking.

The rise in popularity in cigarette smoking in the early nineteenth century led to the appearance of curious creatures called 'cigarette girls'. These were the legions of 'pre-marriage' women, some as young as eight years old, who hand rolled the cigarettes in the tobacco factories of Europe and America. While the tradition associated with cigar making had been for women to roll the leaves on their bare thighs, the emphasis for cigarette rolling was speed. The most famous cigarette girl was Lily Lavendar, AKA Queen of the hand rollers, who worked in a cigarette factory in England. She was recorded as being able to roll 162 individual cigarettes in a thirty-minute window. But mechanisation changed productivity and made smoking mainstream, moving it from a handmade, artisanal cottage industry to a mass produced leisure drug.

In 1880, the American James Bonsack patented an automatic rolling machine which was able to produce 100,000 cigarettes in a ten-hour period. The machine fed tobacco into a compressing cylinder 'where it was matted into a long and continuous rope-like form. This was channelled into yet another tube, where a continuous roll of paper was made to curl around the tobacco cylinder,' says Proctor. The roll would then be cut into individual cigarettes. James Buchanan Duke's American Tobacco Company bought Bonsack's machines and started mass producing cigarettes. He starting producing Duke of Durham, the world's first mass-produced cigarette brand, from the early 1880s. The pack came with a couple of baseball cards, which had a dual purpose: to stiffen the packet and to encourage consumers to collect all the baseball cards in the series, thereby creating repeat customers.

From this point onwards, we see an enormous profusion in the amount of cigarette brands available to consumers. The curing of the tobacco in cigarettes became more sophisticated and this was a boon to brands like Lucky Strike who would emphasise this in their advertising. 'What makes a Lucky taste better? It's toasted, to taste better!' Advertisers

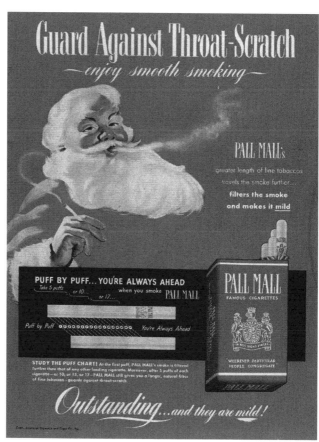

PALL MALL ADVERTISEMENT, 1952

went to great lengths to lure new customers, including kids. Pall Mall had a famous Christmas ad which showed Santa Claus smoking. Winston Cigarettes used Fred and Barney from *The Flintstones* to target children in a TV ad from 1961.

The Marlboro Man, a campaign launched by Philip Morris in 1954, has been described as 'the most powerful mascot in American tobacco marketing in history' by the *Atlantic* magazine. The rugged frontier cowboy helped Marlboro become one of the best-selling brands in the world. The ultra masculine imagery employed by Marlboro was deliberate. Before the 1960s, the smoking of filtered cigarettes such as Marlboro Reds was considered feminine. Real men didn't need

▲ THE MARLBORO MAN, 1977

a filter in their cigarettes, it was thought. After just 12 months of launching their campaign, Marlboro went from a one percent market share to becoming the fourth largest brand in the United States, and the filtered cigarette became the cigarette of popular choice.

The medical consensus on cigarette smoking slowly tempered this type of advertising. A raft of scientific surveys and the US Surgeon General's damning report of 1964 all provided increasing evidence of the link between smoking and cancer. In fact, the expanding life expectancy of people in developed countries played a crucial role in revealing the link with lung cancer. This disease often appears later in life. Before the 1940s, people generally died of something else before lung cancer took hold. But once people started living, on average, into their sixties and seventies, lung cancer was revealed as a major cause of death in smokers. Brandt argues that the infamous 'More doctors smoke Camel' campaign by RJ Reynolds in 1947 'marked an implicit recognition of ongoing concerns about tobacco and serious disease'.

The Nazis were at the vanguard of the anti-tobacco movement during the 1930s. 'Tobacco created an alien allegiance in an era when both mind and body were supposed to belong to the Führer,' writes Robert Proctor in *The Nazi War on Cancer*. Hitler's health minister, Leonardo Conti, was virulently against the smoking of cigarettes. It was seen as a form of laziness or 'lung masturbation' which polluted the purity of the Aryan race and had a negative impact on expectant mothers and on the functioning capabilities of pilots and soldiers of the Reich. Hitler was said to have been particularly buoyed when his propaganda minister, Joseph Goebbels, quit smoking. 'The Führer claimed that Nazism might never have triumphed if he personally had not given up smoking,' writes Proctor. 'He also came to regret allowing his troops to smoke, fearing this had compromised their fighting power.' Despite the magnitude of atrocities committed by the Nazis, they were unusually perceptive about the dangers posed by tobacco use.

32
THE RUNNING SHOE

When shoemaker Adolf Dassler (Adi to his friends) returned to Bavaria after World War One, he would scavenge the countryside for abandoned military paraphernalia for his workshop. Scraps of leather and rubber were fashioned into shoes in the laundry shed at the back of his mother's house. From these humble beginnings this man's name would eventually be amalgamated (Adi + Das) to form one of the most successful shoe companies in the world.

Under the crippling terms of the Versailles Treaty, the German people turned increasingly to sport as a cheap diversion from the economic misery brought on the country. When the Nazis eventually came to power in 1933, Dassler signed up as a party member, purely out of fear that not to do so might hinder his business. The party had incorporated all sports clubs under their own banner. 'The rise of the Nazis unexpectedly increased demand the Dassler's shoes. Hitler regarded sport as an important instrument to encourage discipline and comradeship,' writes Jason Coles in *Golden Kicks: The Shoes that Changed Sport*.

However, Dassler was an opportunist and was only interested in selling shoes. When Jesse Owens, the black American track star, landed in Berlin for the Olympics in 1936, Dassler was determined to put his shoes on the hottest athlete of the competition. Owens was impressed with Dassler's calf leather spiked shoes and went on to win four gold medals in them. When Hitler stormed out of the Olympic stadium in disgust because Owens, a black man, claimed the 100-metre dash, Dassler was in a different mood as he looked on from the stands. 'Dassler could barely contain his pride and excitement,' observes Barbara Smith in *Pitch Invasion: Adidas, Puma and the Making of Modern Sport*. 'The Owens coup anchored the Dasslers' reputation among the world's most prominent athletes.'

Athletic shoes had initially emerged in the late nineteenth century in response to two earlier developments. Firstly, thanks to the efforts of Charles Goodyear, rubber could now be moulded into different shapes. John Boyd Dunlop then managed to bond the vulcanised rubber to a canvas shoe for the first time. Secondly, as the train network expanded, more and more people were taking holidays by the seaside. This led to the development of a more casual cotton or canvas 'sand shoe'. The New Liverpool Rubber Company began selling plimsolls in the 1870s. These were named after a British parliamentarian, Samuel Plimsoll, who introduced the 'Plimsoll line' on cargo ships in 1876. This demarcation represented the maximum load that a ship could safely carry without taking on water. If the load caused the water to creep above the Plimsoll line, then it was unsafe to travel. The seam separating the rubber sole of a shoe from the canvas top reminded people of this, and so the name of the world's first athletic shoe was born.

We generally associate the word 'sneakers' with American culture, but the term has its origins in the British prison system, of all places. Guards wore rubber soled shoes in the late nineteenth century. Prisoners took to describing the silent, creeping shoes as 'sneaks'. Rubber soled shoes were also commonly used by thieves who required quiet footwear for a 'sneaky' getaway. In fact, running shoes often tend to have local colloquialisms. In Munster, for example, running shoes are known as 'tackies', while in old Cork slang they were called 'rubber dollies'.

In the classic 1981 movie *Chariots of Fire*, Harold Abrahams is famously depicted winning the 100-metre sprint at the 1924 Olympics in Paris. It wasn't simply grit and determination which propelled Abrahams over the line. He was the proud owner of one of the most influential running shoes in history, J.W Foster & Sons' running pumps. These Nottinghamshire shoemakers had been making cricket shoes for many years and in the late nineteenth century the owner's grandson Joseph Foster set up a new department of the company and started to adapt them for the running track. Their special design incorporated little metal spikes which offered the athlete greater grip as they ran. 'Demand became so high that he had to move out of the bedroom that had served as his workshop and move next door to create the world's first sports shoe factory,' explains Coles. 'Dubbed the "Olympic Works", athletes now came from far and wide to visit J.W. Fosters and be fitted for a now famous pair of running pumps.' J.W. Fosters would eventually become Reebok, one of the biggest sports brands in the world.

When Fred Perry won his three Wimbledon titles during the 1930s he was perhaps helped on his way to glory by his Green Flash shoes. The Green Flash was launched by Dunlop in 1929 when they entered the tennis market. It featured a herringbone pattern on the sole which offered Perry greater grip on SW19's slippy grass. Perry was regarded as an upstart and an outsider by the Lawn Tennis Association because he wasn't a 'gentleman', in a traditionally upper-class sport. Despite his protestations, he wasn't allowed to profit from his endorsement of Dunlop's shoes as tennis was still strictly amateur at that time. However, his Green Flashes soon became a British sporting icon, like the man himself.

▲ HAROLD ABRAHAMS, WINNER OF THE 100- METRE DASH IN THE 1924 OLYMPICS

▲ FRED PERRY IN 1933

The Converse Rubber Shoe Company started out making shoes for tennis, netball and football until a basketball player named Chuck Taylor took a shine to the product and decided its high-top ankle support was ideal for his emerging sport. He became an ambassador for the company and helped to maximise the design over a number of years. The rubber nose was added to prevent wear and tear from basketball players dragging their feet across the court. In 1932, Converse placed Taylor's signature on the All Star logo, where it remains to this day. 'In many ways, the business relationship between Converse and Chuck Taylor was the first professional sports endorsement contract, and because of it, Converse had the jump on every other basketball shoe in the market,' writes Amber Keysar in *Sneaker Century: A History of Athletic Shoes.*

But when did sports shoes become democratized and outside of the elite? In the early 1960s a running coach from New Zealand by the name of Arthur Lydiard invented jogging. It seems odd to suggest that such a phenomenon could be 'invented', but Lydiard is credited with popularising even-paced running over long distances, for people of all ages. Before this it was unusual to see people running simply for health benefits, rather than for a specific race or to train. Bill Bowerman, the track coach with the University of Oregon, visited Lydiard in New Zealand in 1962 to learn about his new approach. Bowerman's biographer, Kenny Moore, says, 'Lydiard drove them to a rolling, pastoral expanse called Cornwall Park, swarming with a couple of hundred runners. "I thought a cross country race was going on," Bowerman would recall, but they were men, women, children, all ages, all sizes'. Lydiard explained that this was the Auckland Joggers Club, which he had set up a year previously.

Lydiard had borrowed the word 'jogging' from another sport, horse racing. To jog a horse is to exercise it before an event. Lydiard was one of the first people to recognise that running was something which could benefit the health of everyone, not just professional long-distance runners. Bowerman brought Lydiard's jogging concept back to the United States, where *Life* magazine even came to photograph the bizarre activity. He wrote a book about it in 1968 called *Jogging: A Physical Fitness Program for All Ages,* which sold one million copies. The idea of jogging was still so alien to Americans that the front cover of the book actually featured a definition of the term: 'light running and walking'. Soon a worldwide phenomenon ignited the slovenly masses to go out and purchase some running shoes and get moving.

Bowerman was now in a perfect position to exploit the new fad. With his former student Phil Knight, they set up a company called Blue Ribbon Sports in

1964, importing cheap running shoes from Japan, in order to undercut the prices of American brands. Soon Bowerman was designing his own shoes and eventually hit upon the idea of using nylon as a lightweight alternative to heavier, more traditional fabrics. By 1978 they had established Nike as the company's new name.

In the early 1980s, Bowerman and Knight hired a former NASA engineer named Frank Rudy. He began experimenting with the idea of introducing air pockets into the soles of sports shoes to provide extra comfort. Early prototypes were a flop, with the cushions bursting after a single run. However, soon he got the formula right and Nike Air was born.

What really made Nike, with its trademark swoosh logo, a cultural icon was Michael Jordan's endorsement in 1984. The 21-year-old had become a basketball superstar and Nike were keen to capitalise on his success. In his biography of Jordan, Roland Lazenby quotes the man Nike sent to woo him, Sonny Vaccaro. 'That was the first time in my life I'd ever met Michael. We sat down and talked about his going to Nike. He didn't even know about Nike. You have to understand that. And I told him, "Michael, you don't know me, but we're going to build a shoe for you. No one has this shoe". Apparently, all Jordan was interested in getting in return for his endorsement was a car. Eventually he would sign a deal with Nike for $2.5 million which would also give him a five percent cut of every pair of Air Jordan's sold. By 1991 sales of his shoe were running at $200 million per year.'

The Air Jordan was red and black, the colours of the Chicago Bulls. This was in direct contravention of the National Basketball Association's white shoe rule. The NBA immediately banned the Air Jordan and promised to fine Michael $5,000 every time he wore them on court. Nike were delighted with the furore and gladly paid almost half a million dollars in fines over the course of the 1985 season. There's no such thing as bad publicity, I guess. To this day Jordan's deal with Nike is considered to be one of the most influential endorsements in the history of professional sport.

▲ THE AIR JORDAN BY NIKE

Fore Gad ye wretches youl never get my
Stays tight enough go brutes and call John James & Thomas
to help you take care you dont Spoil my Breasts

vi dont you pull by Gar
if you no pull tight my
will have on D——n big
John Ball Belly

Laceing a Dandy

Pub. Jan 26 1819 by T. Tegg 111 Ch

33
underwear

Many years ago I found myself in the famous Rudas Bath House in Budapest. Swimming togs were prohibited so I was given a loincloth to wear. Sporting a loincloth is a very curious and disarming experience for those of us who are used to wearing modern underwear. It is a small rectangle of linen material covering the groin area, with the posterior completely open to the elements. It's a precarious item of modesty – the briefest draught and all is revealed. And of course, as soon as you enter the water, the cloth floats and all is revealed anyway. It is almost completely useless as a shield of modesty, yet this is perhaps the earliest form of underwear that ever existed, and is, therefore, where our story begins.

The loincloth is pervasive in Ancient Egyptian art. The *schenti*, as it was called, was made with cotton or flax and held in place with a belt. It was worn by both men and women. For the poorer classes, it acted not as underwear but as outerwear and nothing was worn over it. But for pharaohs it would have been worn under an outer garment and was, therefore, technically a form of underpants. Tutankhamun was even buried with his collection of loincloths, presumably so his virtue would remain intact in the afterlife.

Braies, or breeches, became popular in the Anglo-Saxon period. At first they were an outer garment but evolved into underwear with the advent of the tunic in Norman times. Braies were baggy drawers (meaning an undergarment that was

◄ ETCHING OF A MAN BEING HELPED INTO HIS UNDERWEAR BY HIS SERVANTS, 1819. WELLCOME COLLECTION *drawn* on). They were mostly made from linen, but in colder climates they were woollen, which sounds rather itchy. A 'braiel', which was a sort of belt, kept them from falling down. Braies became progressively shorter over time, eventually settling around the knee. Woollen hose were then drawn up to cover the entire leg and add an extra layer of warmth.

▲ HENRY VIII WEARING HIS CODPIECE, WORKSHOP OF HANS HOLBEIN THE YOUNGER, 1536-1537

Women of the same period wore a smock, or *chemise* as the Normans called it, which was similar to a modern slip dress. The chemise continued as the undergarment of respectability for women right into the nineteenth century, as evidenced by one in the collection of the Victoria and Albert Museum from 1851. Most people during this period wore their undergarments not just during the day, but also in bed at night. Those who were fussy about hygiene might wash their braies once a week in lye and water.

The codpiece steered the course of underwear in a brand new direction, from the Renaissance period onwards. It started out as a utilitarian flap on the front of a man's braies which allowed him to pee without having to pull down his entire drawers.

Over time, the codpiece enlarged both in size and function, taking on an ever more decorative role. Renaissance fashion historian Elizabeth Currie says it 'became a coin purse, lunch bag, letterbox and handkerchief all in one'. With this came the symbolic nature of 'male genital power' and the codpiece evolved into a symbol of virility. The word codpiece derives from the Middle English word for scrotum. Remember this the next time you order cod in a restaurant.

Hans Holbein's famous portrait of Henry VIII is an evocative showcase of the codpiece. Some historians have speculated that Henry padded out his codpiece in an attempt to cushion his bandaged appendage, which was riddled with syphilis. As Henry VIII was a major tastemaker, soon all men emulated his style and the codpiece became a protruding edifice that was impossible to ignore. It was the first thing one noticed as a man made his entrance into a drawing room.

The bra dates from the late Medieval period when 'breast bags' were developed, essentially a blouse with primitive cups built into them. In 2008 a number of fifteenth century woollen bras were discovered in Lengberg Castle in Austria. Archaeolgist Ula Paulsen describes 'two cups, each made from two pieces of fabric with a centre-joining seam, mounted into a body of slightly coarser material with lacing eyelets on each side and attached straps'. This bra would also have had a square piece of fabric on top to cover up any errant cleavage. The Lengberg bra looks remarkably similar to what is used today, but its evolution was cut short by the arrival of the corset, which then dominated until the end of the nineteenth century.

Olivia Flynt, a dressmaker from Boston, patented the 'bust supporter' in 1876, one of the earliest brassieres, more akin to what we might today describe as a sports bra. She said it was 'especially adapted to ladies having large busts'. Flynt's motivation was to try and offer a more comfortable alternative to the dangerously restrictive corset. She was also an entrepreneur and one of the early adopters of mail order shopping. By the 1880s, she was posting her bras all over the United States and even to Europe. But beating the corset into submission was a near impossible task. Going corset-less was still associated with 'loose' women and even prostitution.

Mary Phelps Jacobs is often credited with patenting the first modern bra, in 1914. She fashioned it out of two handkerchiefs and said her invention was 'so efficient that it may even be worn by persons engaged in violent exercise like tennis'. However, it was never manufactured on a commercial scale. Within a few years the brassiere began to pop up with increasing frequency as a more comfortable alternative to the corset. It made one of its earliest appearances in the *Irish Times* in 1918 when the writer discusses brassieres as 'useful little accessories (that) now come in all the most delicate shades, and are made of silk jersey material, closed with ribbon laces'. After the end of World War One, many different clothing companies innovated different types of brassieres, with the diminutive 'bra' coming into use as a description from as late as 1937.

Eventually, the pointy Torpedo Bra would come to symbolise mid-twentieth century underwear for women. In their book *Uplift: The Bra in America*, historians Jane Farrel-Beck and Colleen Gau, write 'military vocabulary was employed to describe the 1940s brassiere silhouette, the Torpedo, which turned breasts into a pair of nosecones. Long after peace broke out, the Torpedo

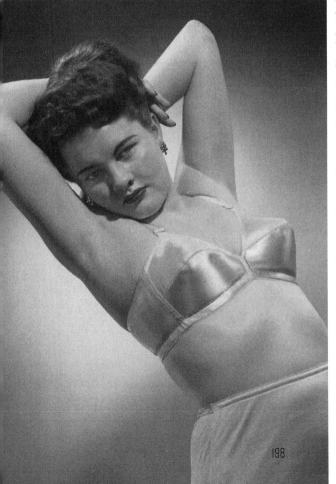

lingered, influencing brassiere design until the late 1950s'. The Torpedo Bra gained iconic status when Marilyn Monroe became perhaps its most famous advocate.

But what happened to men's underwear? The one-piece union suit became the undergarment of choice for gentlemen in the late nineteenth century, so called because it *united* the undershirt and the drawers into one tight and comfortable costume. It was usually made of either

◄ THE TORPEDO BRA

cotton or wool. Union suits had an 'access hatch' at the back. This all sounds rather architectural, but it was a very necessary little flap for when nature called. As a design point, the access hatch was fiercely competitive between different manufacturers of union suits. One outlet, the Imperial Underwear Company, promised that 'The Imperial "drop seat" ensures an absolutely closed crotch under every possible condition,' indicating that inferior union suits may have had loose and unruly access hatches. Union suits remained popular well into the twentieth century. Clark Gable even sported one in his 1940 film *Boom Town*.

Arthur Kneibler, head of marketing with Coopers underwear company, designed the world's first Y-front brief in 1935. He had received a postcard from a friend in the French Riviera depicting a man wearing a skimpy pair of swimming togs. You know the sort … the bronzed European Adonis who is somehow able to get away with wearing a 'budgie smuggler'. He wondered if he could translate this design into a successful and unobtrusive male undergarment. The 'Y' shape on the front of the brief was designed to offer a supportive structure for the genitals and, of course, easy access for peeing. It was made with Lastex, a new type of elastic yarn which allowed the garment to sit snugly against the body. The Y-front was a gamble for Kneibler, but his stock completely sold out within one day. In 1938 his product was launched in London to great acclaim. He called it the Jockey because it was similar in style to a jock strap, which was used by athletes at that time. The product was so successful that they renamed the entire company Jockey, still a market leader to this day.

34

THE FIZZY DRINK

'**O**ne tutti frutti comin' up!' quips Rock Hudson in the 1952 movie *Has Anybody Seen my Gal*. Hudson plays a soda jerk. There were half a million people employed as soda jerks in pharmacies and parlours across the United States during the early to mid-twentieth century. Jerks were white-capped, wise cracking soda fountain attendants serving up lime rickeys and cherry fizz to thirsty patrons. 'America's soda jerk became the pop culture star of the Gilded Age,' says Michael Karl Witzel in *The American Drive-In*.

Because of the difficulties in maintaining the carbonation of water and the primitive nature of America's bottling industry in the late nineteenth century, the best way to enjoy a fizzy drink was to go to a specialised soda fountain. Americans Jacob Ebert and George Dulty patented the world's first soda fountain

SODA FOUNTAIN, 1960S ▶

▲ THE PALACE SODA FOUNTAIN, TAMPA FLORIDA, 1925

in 1833. As the nineteenth century progressed, soda fountains sprang up all over the country, usually located in pharmacies because carbonated water was initially regarded as a health tonic. They soon began to take the shape of little parlours or saloons, with long white marble counters and ornate copper fountains with spigots and taps to whip up every flavour imaginable. 'Soda fountains became 1,000-seat affairs in some cities, and with the onset of Prohibition many saloons, ornate to begin with, became soda fountains,' according to the *New York Times*. Soda jerks became highly skilled and well remunerated attendants in the pharmacies, so much so that they unionised as early as the 1880s. Once prohibition was introduced in 1920, most of the newly out-of-work barmen transferred their skills and became soda jerks. They became affectionately known as soda *jerks* because of the jerking action which was required to pump the soda water from the fountain.

But when did artificial carbonation begin? The English philosopher and chemist Joseph Priestley, best known for discovering oxygen, invented soda water in 1767. He lived near a brewery and became interested in the 'fixed air' given off by yeast during the fermentation process. It was this fixed air, or carbon dioxide as we would describe it today, that he wished to develop artificially. Naturally volcanic spring water was prized for its minerals and ability to aid digestion. Priestly wondered if he might be able to reproduce it for people who didn't live near these types of waters. He started mixing sulphuric acid and chalk together to create carbon dioxide. He kept this in a pig's bladder and then managed to introduce it into still water to make what he described as 'aerated water'. Although his initial experiments only yielded a weakly carbonated drink, he had unwittingly kicked off a beverage revolution.

The German drinks manufacturer Johann Jacob Schweppe took the next important step and developed a device in 1783 which could readily carbonate water using a compression pump. Eventually, flavours began to be added to carbonated water to make a pleasant and refreshing drink. This was the birth of the fizzy drink as we know it today.

From the mid-nineteenth century, pharmacies began to sell their sodas as medicinal concoctions to help with ailments. People would pop into their local drug store for a 'pick me up' or to 'get some pep'. Cocaine and caffeine started to be added by pharmacists to help with headaches. At this time, stimulants were seen as healthy and cocaine was entirely legal until its prohibition in 1914. The cocaine caused rebound headaches which then spurred customers to return to the pharmacy for another 'hit'.

Dr John Smith Pemberton introduced a beverage called Pemberton's French Wine Coca in the 1870s. Pemberton had become a morphine addict after suffering an injury during the Civil War. He wanted to create a stimulant, so he introduced cocaine to his beverage and described it as 'a most wonderful invigorator of sexual organs'. However, his home county in the state of Georgia was a very early adopter of alcohol prohibition in the 1890s, so he was forced to remove the wine from his product. He replaced it with sugar syrup and renamed it Coca Cola: The Temperance Beverage. His company soon hit on the idea of distributing their wonder product through the soda fountain network which was already in place across the country. By 1899 it started to be sold in bottles for the first time. This decision made Coca Cola available to the black community who had been barred from entering the segregated soda fountains.

However, the addition of cocaine in soda soon became controversial. It started to develop a negative reputation and the media picked up on this. In February 1902 the *Los Angeles Times* ran an article with the headline 'They thirst for cocaine ... Soda Fountain Fiends Multiplying.' The article explored the spread of soda addiction in the city, writing that 'a great many people in Los Angeles have contracted the coca cola habit'. In response to this shift in public opinion, Coca Cola began removing cocaine from their beverage in 1903 and replaced it with extra sugar and caffeine.

A cola war erupted between Coca Cola and its upstart nemesis Pepsi Cola during the 1920s. The much larger and more established Coca Cola used its power and leverage to intimidate its rival. However, Pepsi's owner, Charles Guth, eventually hit on a bright idea. He realised that he could attract cash poor victims of the Great Depression by selling 12-ounce bottles of his product for the same price as 6-ounce Coca Cola bottles. As his product was basically just carbonated sugar water, the difference in doubling the amount of liquid was negligible. His decision was an instant success and suddenly Coca Cola had a viable rival, a rival that went on to play a small yet significant role in Cold War diplomacy.

In 1957, as tensions between the United States and the Soviet Union fizzled, the Eisenhower administration decided to put on an exhibition of American life in Moscow to showcase the positive sides of his country's culture and economy to Soviet citizens. Coca Cola was invited to attend, but declined on the grounds that their product had been demonised by the USSR as symbolic of the West's capitalist evils. Pepsi took the bold decision to take their place at the exhibition, wisely eyeing an opportunity to expand their market. Donald Kendall, who was representing Pepsi at the exhibition, had convinced Vice President Richard Nixon to encourage Soviet Premier Nikita Kruschev to sample his product. As the two leaders toured the exhibition hall in Moscow, Nixon gently steered Kruschev over to the Pepsi stand. 'Kendall handed the Soviet leader two Pepsis. The first was a Pepsi made in the United States, he told the Communist leader; the second was one made in the USSR for this exhibition. Kruschev tried both and inevitably declared the Soviet-made Pepsi to be superior before ordering a second Communist cola as they were bathed in camera flashes,' writes Tristan

▲ SOVIET PREMIER NIKITA KRUSCHEV TASTES PEPSI AS US VICE PRESIDENT RICHARD NIXON LOOKS ON

Donovan in *Fizz: How Soda Shook up the World*. Eventually, after many years of negotiation, Pepsi's audacious move paid off when it became the first ever American consumer product to go on sale in the Soviet Union, opening up a vast new market for the soda company.

▲ LAUREL AND HARDY

THE BED

The bed is a microcosm of life, a place where sleep, sex, birth and death have all played out for centuries. It is a place where we spend one third of our lives, a warm refuge punctuating the transition from one day to the next. It is also an object through which we can understand how people live. This is why it is used so widely in books, movies and television, not simply as something that people sleep in, but as something which offers us an insight into the characters' lives.

In Roald Dahl's *Charlie and the Chocolate Factory*, all four of the grandparents share the only bed in the house. This reflects the poverty of the family and fuels Charlie's dreams of a different type of existence. It also draws a sharp contrast with the extravagance and glamour of Willy Wonka's chocolate factory.

Many male comedy duos over the years, from Laurel and Hardy to Morecambe and Wise, shared a bed, undermining modern assumptions of the relationship between the bed and sex.

Basil and Sybil Fawlty had separate beds, echoing the prudishness of middle England in the 1970s. Conversely, John Lennon and Yoko Ono spent a week in a bed in an attempt to draw attention to the Vietnam War. The bedroom is a place of frightful horror in movies such as *Nightmare on Elm Street* and *The Exorcist*, where the bed becomes a stage for the audience's worst nightmares. 'From birth to death, it is the theater of existence, or at least its dressing room; the place where the mask is removed; the body undressed and relinquished to the emotions,' writes Michelle Perot in *Bedroom: An Intimate History*.

THE GOLDEN BED.

▲ VICTORIAN BLACK AND WHITE ENGRAVING OF THE
GOLDEN BED OF SEVENTEENTH CENTURY BRAHAN
CASTLE, DINGWALL, SCOTLAND

In the Anglo-Saxon period, beds often doubled as tables during the daytime. In fact, this is where the term 'bed and board' comes from. A bed was a collection of wooden boards which could be assembled in different ways for different functions. It was during the medieval period that we see the increasing elevation of the bed off the floor to keep the occupant away from the damp and the scurrying rodents below. A wooden frame was built to hold a mattress or sack filled with hay (hence the expression 'hit the hay'). It was not unusual for men to sleep together in a bed. This was not necessarily sexual in nature. Rather it was a way to keep warm and save on space.

In 1187, a chronicler noted that Richard the Lionheart and King Philip II of France got along so well (despite their initial bargy over a territorial disagreement in Normandy) that at night time 'a bed did not separate them'. Richard's sexuality has been debated for decades, but some scholars believe that their sharing a bed was simply a bold diplomatic gesture that was typical of the time, a way of showing your trust for another man. In an interview on the topic with the *Telegraph*, historian John Gillingham argued that sharing a bed 'was an accepted political act, nothing sexual about it; just two politicians literally getting into bed together, a bit like a modern-day photo opportunity'. This may have worked in the twelfth century, but it's hard to imagine the French president and the British prime minister hopping into bed together for a quick press conference today.

Bundling was a curious type of bedroom courtship during the medieval period in England. According to historian Lucy Worsley, bundling meant that a young man and a young woman were permitted by their parents to share a bed for a night to get to know one another and see if they might be a good match. The idea was that they would talk through the night and avoid any 'shenanigans'. Inevitably, this was a recipe for disaster. 'Sometimes they were even tied down, or a board was placed down the middle of their bed ... Bundling was a step along the way towards your spouse being a matter of personal choice, rather than someone picked out for you by your parents,' writes Worsley.

By the Renaissance period, the bed gets increasingly tall, to the point that it sometimes required a stool to climb into. This was for two reasons. Firstly, the higher the bed the further you were from the cold and damp of the ground and the closer you were to the warm air which rose to the top of the room. Secondly, a higher bed symbolised your social rank, as the poor often slept on the floor.

Before the advent of the four-poster in the fifteenth century, beds often had canopies attached to the ceiling. The four-poster was simply a development on this idea, turning the canopy into drapes falling from the beams of the bed structure itself. The drapes helped to retain the heat during winter nights, keep vermin out and, of course, add luxury and status to one's bed. English poet Edith Sitwell once remarked 'All women should have a day a week in bed'. She loved spending time in her enormous four-poster bed so much that she allowed herself to be photographed taking her breakfast in it in 1932.

Perhaps the most famous example of a four-poster is the Great Bed of Ware, which dates from 1590. The town of Ware was a day's journey from London at that time and was a popular place for people to spend the night on their way to Cambridge, according to the Victoria and Albert Museum, where the bed can still be seen today. It is likely that it was designed for an inn in the town. It is made from beautifully carved oak, reaches three metres in width and could hold four couples. It has four mattresses of plaited rush, unspun wool, feathers and down.

Four-poster beds such as the one in Ware often feature male and female iconography in the wood work to illustrate its reproductive role in a marriage. Indeed, one of the four-posters in Russborough House in Co. Wicklow

▲ THE GREAT BED OF WARE, LATE SIXTEENTH CENTURY.
© VICTORIA AND ALBERT MUSEUM, LONDON

features an image of Cupid and his arrow. The Bed of Ware became so famous that Shakespeare alluded to it in his play *Twelfth Night*. But why was the Bed of Ware so ludicrously big? Was it designed as a gimmick to attract visitors to to the town of Ware? Or perhaps it was simply a way of accommodating as many people as possible in a single bed? It was not uncommon at that time for all members of a family to share a bed. What a great way to save on space (if not privacy).

Bedroom politics were elaborate during the reign of Henry VIII. An army of staff was required to arrange a visit by the king to the bedroom of his wife. Guards cleared the corridors of the court for Henry's long procession to her quarters and then they would engage in a disrobing ceremony before hopping into the bed together. Despite his extramarital affairs and multiple wives, Henry was very conscious of bedroom privacy and would even demand that two guards slept on pallets outside the marital chamber. Some kings even had a truckle bed under their own, where their most favoured servant or even their Groom of the Stool (see Chapter 27, The Toilet) would sleep. The drapes hanging from a four-poster helped to create added privacy.

The security of the royal bed was also a concern. On the night of Henry's marriage to Catherine of Aragon, John de Vere, the Lord Chamberlain, had to inspect the bedclothes for any hidden weapons or objects that could cause injury. After a Tudor wedding, a priest would accompany the king and his new wife to the bedroom. Spiced wine would be drunk to fortify the couple for the energetic tasks ahead of them. The priest would then offer a blessing, explains Tracy Borman in *The Private Lives of the Tudors*. 'The onlookers were often slow to leave. Sometimes, they demanded to see the naked legs of the couple touching, which in some cases was accepted as a sign of consummation ... It was a crude reminder that the royal body was a property of the state.'

The next morning, the bloodied bed sheets would be displayed as further proof of consummation, as is what happened to the bed linens belonging to Isabelle of Castile in 1469. This gave rise to the expression 'to air one's dirty linen in public'.

In the seventeenth century there was an increase in the number of beds in homes in England. Beds in wealthy households were generally made of either mahogany or ash. Some were box bedsteads, literally a large cupboard with a bed which had closing doors to keep draughts out and provide a level of privacy. The mattress, as defined by Samuel Johnson in his 1755 dictionary as 'a kind of quilt made to lie upon', became increasingly diverse in style in this period. The more expensive ones were stuffed with linen or cotton ticking while cheaper ones were made with straw. The mattress sat on a series of ropes which criss-crossed the bed frame. These tended to sag and therefore had to be tightened each evening before going to sleep. This may have sparked the salutation 'sleep tight'.

With the introduction of new materials during the Industrial Revolution, Samuel Kettle patented the coil sprung mattress in 1865, immediately creating a much more comfortable sleeping experience because the springs spread the weight of the individual more evenly across the bed.

The politics of the bed came into stark focus in the twentieth century. The British Board of Film Classification was set up in 1912. Even at this early date the influence of films was seen as a threat to morality. When Irish journalist T.P. O'Connor became the board's president in 1916 he introduced 43 scenes which were to be prohibited, including 'men and women in bed together.' The idea of a man and woman sharing a bed was as abhorrent as 'cruelty to animals' and 'subjects dealing with India, in which British Officers are seen in an odious light,' both of which were also banned.

William H. Hays, a former Postmaster General in the United States, was given the job of moral arbiter in Hollywood in the 1920s. By 1930 the Hays Code had been published. It was one of the earliest attempts at a censorship system for movies in America. The *New Yorker*'s film critic David Denby explains that 'the Code prohibited profanity, licentious or suggestive nudity, sexual perversions, and rape. But one of the products of long and deep thought was the elimination of any suggestion that a man and a woman ever went to bed together'. For this reason, men and women slept in separate beds for the following 20 years of movie making in Hollywood. Even the long married characters played by Spencer Tracy and Katharine Hepburn in *Adam's Rib* (1949) had separate beds, as a result of the Code.

The Hays Code went so far as to demand that if a man and woman were sitting on a bed together, or engaged in a romantic scene, the woman had to keep at least one foot on the floor at all times, to ensure that there was no depiction of sex.

© P&G 1986

THE WET STOPS HERE.

Babies are thrilled with Pampers® and its blue waist shield. And for good reason. Because this unique blue waist shield helps keep wetness from leaking up better than any diaper with a regular waist ever did before. So Moms are thrilled. Because they know that means drier T-shirts, drier sheets... and a drier baby from top to bottom!

KEEPS BABIES DRIER FROM TOP TO BOTTOM.

For your Softouches Catalog, send your name and address to: Pampers Baby Catalog, P.O. Box 8634, Clinton, Iowa 52736.

▲ 1986 PAMPERS ADVERTISEMENT

36
THE NAPPY

'**A**nother bear the ewer, the third a diaper.' This is thought to be among the earliest references to a diaper in the English language. When Shakespeare wrote the word into *The Taming of the Shrew*, in the late sixteenth century, he was probably referring to a type of linen or cotton cloth with a ribboned pattern. The word comes from the Greek 'diaspros', meaning 'thoroughly white'. It was a white square of fabric that would eventually come to describe the swaddling bands worn by a baby.

Nowadays, we associate the word diaper with American English, but originally this was a word used in England and in Ireland. It was brought to America by the colonists. Indeed, as late as 1895, the *Longford Leader* newspaper was offering advice on 'the best way we have found of holding up the diaper of the baby just learning to walk'. The article offers a fascinating insight into the difficulties of diapering at that time. It involved the making of buttonholes and the sewing of the diaper to a petticoat worn by the baby to keep the whole arrangement together. The article continued, in as condescending a tone as it could muster, 'A busy little mother who thinks baby ought to play on the ground has made a half dozen large diapers of coloured flannel'.

The word diaper stuck in America while 'napkin' took hold in England in the early twentieth century, eventually settling on the diminutive 'nappy' from the late 1920s. Napkin is derived from the Old French 'nappe', meaning tablecloth and the Middle English 'kin' which means 'little'. How did something we wipe our mouths with come to describe something babies routinely defecate into? The two activities seem like chalk and cheese, yet share the same name. It appears that the definition of a napkin as a 'small cloth' could be applied to either situation.

By 1910, rubber pants had arrived but were unpopular because they caused nappy rash. Poorer families continued to use anything they could get their hands on, including used flour sacks bound around the baby's bottom. Most families continued to use cloth options. Cleaning nappies was tough, nasty work. Boiling and the use of chemicals helped, but often caused rashes.

During the Second World War, a curious service was launched in many cities in America, attempting to fill a new niche in the market. In her *History of Diapers and Diapering*, Bernice Krafchik explains that 'when women joined the workforce alongside men, they did not have the time or energy to manage the enormous task of washing diapers at home after work. It was at this time that diaper laundry services first made an appearance'. Each week the service would visit your home, delivering your sterilised nappies and picking up the soiled ones. 'Diaper laundry services refined diaper laundering to eleven wash cycles with detergent, the last four with boiling water alone.' Indeed, diapers were at a premium during World War Two. Because of the war effort, there simply wasn't enough cloth to make the amount of diapers required by the population. 'Babies Must Make 2 Diapers Last as Long as 3 in Normal Times,' declared an article in the *New York Times* in January 1945. The situation was so dire that 'millions of yards of washed flour and sugar bags ... were sold mainly for diaper use'.

However, the big problem remained: how do you waterproof a baby so that you don't have to change the nappy every time it gets soiled? Connecticut native Marion Donovan contributed greatly to the evolution of nappies in the mid-twentieth century. She was fed up to the hilts with leaking diapers and wanted to find a solution. She tore down her waterproof shower curtain and fashioned it into a diaper shape. She then stuffed the seat of the diaper with absorbent paper. She called it 'the Boater' because apparently her husband observed that it didn't leak, just like a decent boat. She spent three years perfecting her design, settling on nylon as the best waterproof material. It was designed in such a way that a cloth diaper could be comfortably worn under the Boater itself. She even tried it on her neighbours' babies to test for different sizes.

Donovan also filed a patent for plastic snaps as a safer alternative to safety

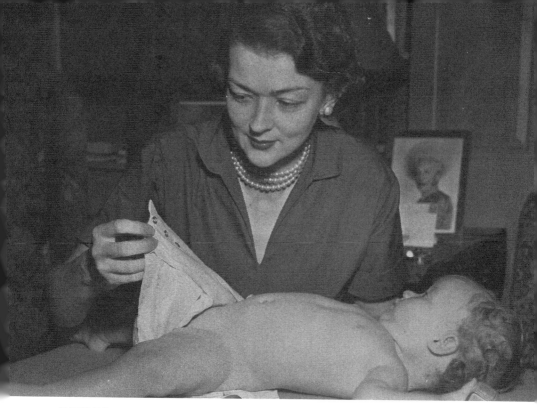

▲ MARION DONOVAN DEMONSTRATING HER NEW DIAPER INNOVATION. ARCHIVES CENTRE, NATIONAL MUSEUM OF AMERICAN HISTORY, SMITHSONIAN INSTITUTION

pins, to keep the diaper secured on the baby. She brought her invention to countless manufacturers but the men who ran the companies dismissed her ideas. Much later in life, in an interview with Barbara Walters in 1975, Donovan recalled, 'I went to all the big names that you can think of, and they said, "We don't want it. No woman has asked us for that. They're very happy and they buy all our baby pants." So I went into manufacturing myself'. Eventually, Saks of Fifth Avenue in New York began to stock her range. They quickly sold out and within a few years she sold her patents for $1 million. Her invention was so revolutionary that it made the newspapers, appearing on the front of the *Miami Sunday News*. They gave it a brilliant review, writing, 'Even if there is more moisture present than the diaper can absorb, it remains in the diaper cover without leaking, unless you turn the baby completely upside down'. Hardly to be recommended.

The disposable nappy was slow to develop. A company called Robinsons of Chesterfield in the UK had developed 'Destroyable Babies' Napkins' as early as the 1930s. Very little information remains about this product so it can't have been a tremendous success. In 1942, a Swedish company called Paulistrom was the first to introduce absorbent pads made from creped tissue paper. However, the disposable nappy didn't truly take off until a chemical engineer with Proctor and Gamble, Victor Mills, launched Pampers in 1961.

Proctor and Gamble had purchased a paper pulp plant and tasked Mills, already a granddad at this stage in his life, with coming up with an efficient and comfortable disposable diaper. Mills' Eureka moment came when he realised that cellulose fibres, obtained from wood pulp, would be more absorbent than paper. 'When Mr. Mills turned his energy to diapers in the 1950s, it was his grandchildren who took their turn as test subjects,' wrote the *New York Times* in their obituary of the great nappy innovator. 'While driving his daughter's three children home from a vacation in Maine, Mr. Mills tried out Pampers prototypes on one of them … Apparently, they worked.'

However, making a commercial success of his invention was another matter. Mills tested the product in Illinois but it wasn't a success. While mothers were

DISPOSABLE NAPPY ▲

satisfied that the product worked, they were not willing to shell out for an expensive luxury like this. Proctor and Gamble went back to the drawing board and over a number of years managed to bring the price down to 5 ½ cent per nappy, by 1966. It was in this year that they rolled the product our nationally. Pampers transformed the nappy industry from cloth to disposable within ten years. By 1973 the disposable nappy market had grown from $10 million a year to $370 million a year, in the US alone.

No fol-de-rol a girl can wear   *Has such allure as shining hair!*

No other Shampoo
leaves hair so lustrous, and yet so easy to manage

Only Drene with Hair Conditioner reveals up to 33% more lustre than soap . . . yet leaves hair so easy to arrange, so alluringly smooth!

Does your hair look dull, slightly mousy?

Maybe it's just because you're washing it with soap or soap shampoos . . . letting soap film hide the glorious natural lustre and color brilliance. Change to Drene with Hair Conditioner. Drene never leaves any dulling film. That's why it reveals up to 33% more lustre than any soap shampoo!

Does your hair-do require constant fiddling?

Men don't like this business of running a comb through your hair in public! Fix your hair so it stays put! And remember Drene with Hair Conditioner leaves hair wonderfully easy to manage, right after shampooing! No other shampoo leaves hair so lustrous, yet so easy to arrange!

Sssssshhhhh! But have you dandruff?

Too many girls have! And what a pity. For unsightly dandruff can be easily controlled if you shampoo regularly with Drene. Drene with Hair Conditioner removes every trace of embarrassing flaky dandruff the very first time you use it!

NEWEST ACCESSORY TRICK is this ribbon "choker" tied fetchingly in front. Wonderful dress up the new, low-necked evening sweater. Newest hair-do trick is this braided arrangement with the ends of the front hair turned over the braids, on top, to form a smooth shining puff! Extra lustre and smoothness due to Drene Shampoo with Hair Conditioner.

Drene Shampoo
with
Hair Conditioner
Product of Procter & Gamble

Guaranteed by Good Housekeeping

MAKE A DATE WITH *Glamour*

Tonight . . . don't put it off . . . shampoo your hair the new glamour way! Use Drene with Hair Conditioner! Get the combination of beauty benefits that only this wonderful improved shampoo can give! ✓ Extra lustre . . . up to 33% more than with soap or soap shampoos! ✓ Manageable hair . . . easy to comb into smooth shining neatness! ✓ Complete removal of flaky dandruff! Ask for Drene Shampoo with Hair Conditioner.

37
SHAMPOO

'There is scarcely a malady which, at some point of its progress, is not susceptible of relief from the Vapour and Shampooing processes,' read an advertisement in the *Brighton Gazette* in July 1860. An Indian immigrant by the name of Sake Dean Mahomed, a shampooing expert operating a public vapour bath in Brighton, had brought the practice back from India as early as 1814. But this type of shampooing, which the Victorians were so enamoured with, was very different to how we regard the practice today.

The word shampoo comes from the Hindi word 'champo', meaning a head massage using oils. Mahomed, and his Irish wife, Jane Daly, had become so celebrated for their practice that Sake eventually became 'Shampooing Surgeon' to both George IV and later, William IV. 'For attendance on such noble patients,

SAKE DEEN MOHAMED, ▶
THE FATHER OF SHAMPOOING,
COLOURED LITHOGRAPH BY T.M.
BAYNES. WELLCOME COLLECTION

he charged a royal rate of 1 guinea each for a shampoo and vapor bath,' writes Michael Fisher, the editor of Mahomed's memoirs. Over time, the word shampoo slowly came to describe the massaging not just of oils but other cleaning ointments into the hair too.

Humans produce a natural oil called sebum which protects the structure of the hair. This oil tends to attract dust and dirt and then needs to be cleaned. In ancient times people turned to natural saponins to clean the hair. The Egyptians used the soapwort plant. When this was added to water it developed a lathery foam. Animal fats would be added to the mixture to help condition the hair and fragrant oils to lend a pleasant aroma to the concoction. The Ancient Celts mixed goat fat with the ashes of burned birch or beech trees. These ashes act as a type of lye (sodium hydroxide). Lye causes saponification, creating soap.

The home of the most successful and influential soap for use in hair was Aleppo in modern day Syria. Although the first written account of Aleppo soap dates to 8AD, it probably existed long before that. It was developed using a mix of olive oil, laurel and lye. After the ingredients were boiled together, the mixture would be poured into shallow pools. Gradually the chemical reaction between the fat of the oil and the lye would mature into a solid brick of soap over a seven-month period, turning from green to brown in the process. Aleppo soap became known for its mild and less corrosive

ALEPPO SOAP ▲

cleaning properties and was therefore ideal for using in hair.

The Crusaders brought the genius of Aleppo soap to Spain from the eleventh century. Laurel, a crucial ingredient of Aleppo soap, was in short supply, but the city of Castile had enormous resources of olive oil. It was here that the European soap industry kicked off, producing a white soap which became popular with the Spanish royal family. Soon, Castile soap became the hair cleanser of choice across Europe.

By the fourteenth century, Castile soap had arrived in England. Soap shavings were boiled with herbs to create a naturally fragrant liquid with which to clean the body and hair. Previously, soap had been made using animal fats in England, but the influence of Castile soap caused the switch to olive oil.

During the Elizabethan period very fine powders were combed through the hair to absorb any excess oils. Courtiers and noblewomen attempted to emulate Elizabeth I, a famous red head, by dying their hair. 'One type of hair dye and conditioner was made from a mixture of rhubarb juice and oil of vitriol (sulfuric acid),' explains Victoria Sherrow in her *Encyclopedia of Hair*. 'Since vitriol was a corrosive agent, the use of this product could cause hair loss.'

In the eighteenth century the wig was king. At the beginning of the century wigs were exceptionally long and ornate, sometimes stretching as low as the bum. These wigs required as many as ten heads of natural hair to make one single peruke. A less expensive option was to purchase one made from horsehair. But wigs were dirty old things if they were not kept clean. First, sand or mill dust would be combed through the hair to absorb excess grease. If a wig was particularly filthy it would be boiled in a saucepan for a few hours. Then a special pomade was made up. A typical recipe would include a pound of pig suet and a pound of sheep suet, mixed with boiled apples. Macassar oil or rosewood oil would also be added for fragrance. This greasy mixture would be fingered into the peruke before a white powder was applied using a bellows. 'Wigs went out of fashion for good (except in the law courts) at the end of the century, when powder taxes and sympathy for French revolutionaries made short, natural hair the rage,' according to Kirsten Olsen in *Daily Life in 18th century England*.

Good Housekeeping magazine was still recommending the use of Castile soap for hair care as late as 1889. One particular form of Castile soap called Kirk's

Juvenile Toilet Soap advertised itself in 1890 as 'Delightful, delicately perfumed, refreshing and healthful for ladies and children'. But the Victorians concocted all manner of surfactants for the hair. If you couldn't afford to hire a shampooing surgeon such as Sake Dean Mahomed then you simply made up your own formulas. Egg yolks were often worked into the scalp, the protein helping to nourish the hair.

Godey's Lady's Book of 1867 recommended strong black tea for good hair care. 'Rub it into the roots every evening before going to bed, with a little sponge, and every morning do the same. I generally use it, and recommend it to all ladies desirous of having a full head of hair.' The *American Frugal Housewife* (1833) instead proclaimed rum to be the surfactant of choice. 'New England rum, constantly used to wash the hair, keeps it very clean, and free from disease, and promotes its growth a great deal more than Macassar oil. Brandy is very strengthening to the roots of the hair; but it has a hot, drying tendency.'

By the mid-nineteenth century it was becoming more socially acceptable for men to wash their hair. A gentleman's moustache required greater tending, however. A black pomatum, a type of hair oil, would be applied to the 'whiskers' to style them and keep their shape.

The major problem with soaps, which most people were still using in their hair by the early twentieth century, was the oily residue that was left after washing. It left a dull film of scum and people wanted something that would make their hair feel truly clean. Procter and Gamble, of Ohio, launched the world's first soap free alternative in 1935. It was called Royal Drene Shampoo. A 1937 ad claimed, 'It isn't oil, it isn't soap – it isn't anything you've heard of before'. The advertising campaign emphasised how the product could save time and cut out the laborious hair care processes that people were used to at that time. '"What?" you say, "no special rinses; no vinegar, lemon or after-rinses to 'cut' the lather?" No – they are not necessary – just a thorough dousing in clear water!' Drene came in a glass bottle, similar in shape to a ketchup bottle, and cost $2. With inflation this would be a whopping $35 in today's money. The company recommended using it once a week. Through the introduction of synthetic cleaning agents, Proctor and Gamble had moved haircare away from soap and paved the way for a brand new industry.

The elimination of dandruff was a major concern for consumers. Vosene launched the world's first successful product in this area in 1949. The active ingredient to combat dandruff in their Original Medicated Shampoo was coal tar, which really stung if it went in the eyes. Proctor and Gamble were also working to develop an anti-dandruff formula, launching Head and Shoulders in 1961. After ten years of research, the company's scientists found a successful active ingredient to tackle dandruff: pyrithione zinc. To this day Head and Shoulders is the biggest selling shampoo in the world with annual sales in excess of 29 million bottles per annum.

1957 BRITISH ADVERTISEMENT FOR SUNSILK SHAMPOO

AMERICAN RED CROSS

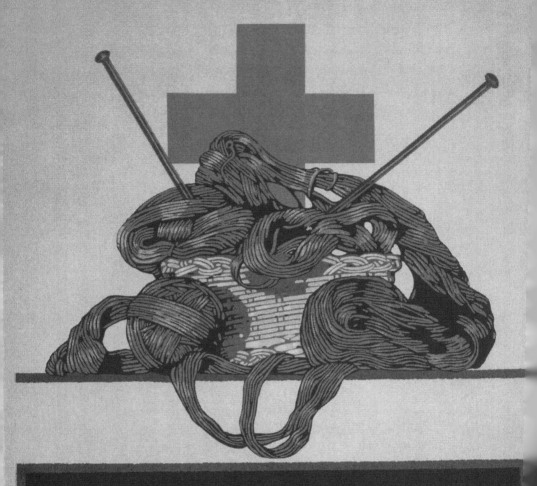

OUR BOYS NEED SOX
KNIT YOUR BIT

38
THE SOCK

In the sitcom *Blackadder,* Hugh Laurie's Prince Regent bemoans the absence of socks in his wardrobe. 'You know, Blackadder, for me socks are like sex. Tons of it about and I never seem to get any.' This was a period when men's stockings were very visible due to the knee-length breeches then in fashion, and the Prince would have taken every opportunity to display a shapely leg. In Thomas Lawrence's 1816 portrait of the real George IV (the former Prince Regent), he is wearing white stockings with a Knight's garter on his left calf. Clearly he had finally managed to find his socks at that stage. In another portrait, by David Wilkies, he wears fancy pink and white tartan socks with tassels. It wasn't until the mid-nineteenth century that full-length trousers made men's socks almost invisible. But in the time of the Prince Regent, choosing which socks to wear was a major sartorial decision for the nobility. But were socks always a part of our dressing ritual?

The Ancient Greeks wrapped their feet and ankles with matted animal hair from the eighth century BC. Other ancient cultures used woven leathers and animal pelts. The word itself derives from the Latin *soccus,* which describes a loose fitting slipper worn by comedic stage actors during Ancient Roman times. 'What had begun as a style for the stage had become a style popular with the audience as well,' according to the authors of *The World of Roman Costume.* 'By the end of the third century the soft indoor slipper had become quite popular.' Gradually the *soccus* came to be associated with an undergarment for the foot,

◄ THE RED CROSS POSTER TO ENCOURAGE CIVILIANS TO KNIT SOCKS
   FOR THE WAR EFFORT, CIRCA 1918

worn under an outer shoe, for comfort and warmth. The Edict of Diocletian offers an insight into the types of socks that became available for the general public in Roman times. Six different types of socks are listed, from gilded socks to Babylonian purple.

One of the best preserved pairs of ancient socks can be seen in the collection of the Victoria and Albert Museum. Dating from between the third and fourth centuries, they were discovered along the banks of the River Nile in a Greek settlement called Oxyrhynchus. In what would today be described as a major fashion faux pas, the people of this area wore their socks with sandals, necessitating a divided toe. This gives them a cloven shape. They are a remarkably well preserved red woolen sock, made with the *nalbinding* technique, often referred to as single needle knitting. This type of stitching facilitates an elastic effect which makes the socks tight fitting on the foot. The top of each sock has an overlapping slit at the centre for fastening or tying so the socks didn't slip down the leg.

▲ PAIR OF WOOLLEN SOCKS, THIRD/FOURTH
CENTURY DISCOVERED ALONG THE RIVER NILE.
© VICTORIA AND ALBERT MUSEUM, LONDON

From the Middle Ages through to the eighteenth century, the sock became increasingly long as men's breeches got shorter, until they eventually became stockings. Garters began to be used, initially by men, in order to keep stockings up. As reported by Ida Tomshinsky in her history of socks, garters came to be highly decorative, with ribbons and even bell attachments.

In the fifteenth century the French and Italian aristocracies introduced silk stockings which could stretch and breathe and help show off one's legs. 'Silk of course was the choice of royalty as the discovery of the New World opened up trade in this rare and luxurious fiber,' writes Tomshinsky. By the late eighteenth century, Englishmen were bringing these continental fashions back to England from the Grand Tour. These men were known as 'macaronis' and often sported fancy stockings. 'A shapely leg beneath the knee breeches and striped stockings was also a requirement of macaroni fashion,' writes Shaun Cole in *The Story of Men's Underwear*. 'For those whose legs were not well-formed, help was at hand. False calf pads, made from parchment or flannel, could be strapped onto the leg under a man's stockings.'

During Elizabethan times, the Queen introduced new Sumptuary Laws to regulate the expenditure and class system of the general population. Elizabeth I was determined to segregate fashion according to social rank. In England the Sumptuary Laws focused especially on men's fashions. The narcissism of exuberant clothing on the wrong 'type' of person was seen as a threat to the moral fibre of the nation.

The 1560s Articles for the Execution of the Statutes of Apparel forbade anyone from wearing hose of 'monstrous and outrageous greatness'. The laws concerning hosiery were bizarrely specific, setting a limit of one and a half yards of cloth per pair of hose. Only one other fabric apart from linen could be used in a stocking. However, some ranks were exempt: 'Neither any man under the degree of a baron to wear within his hose any velvet, satin, or other stuff'. One of the motivations of the Sumptuary Laws was to attack a perceived vanity in men. The proclamation reads, 'The excess of apparel and the superfluity of unnecessary foreign wares (has led to) the wasting and undoing of a great number of young gentlemen ... seeking by show of apparel to be esteemed as gentlemen who (are) allured by the vain show of those things'. Of course, Elizabeth herself had no qualms about her own vanity. Upon her death her wardrobe contained 3,000 dresses and 80 wigs.

The evolution of the sock changed forever in 1589 when Englishman William Lee invented the stocking frame (hence the word 'stocking' to describe socks). This was the world's first knitting machine. His machine could produce a pair of socks six times faster than by hand. He approached Elizabeth I about getting a patent for his invention, but was rebuffed as she was under tremendous pressure from the Hosier's Guild. They were rightly terrified that mechanisation would render their trade obsolete. However, Lee travelled to France and was rewarded with a patent from Henry IV.

We cannot forget the central function of the sock. It was not purely about showcasing your wealth and status. By the early sixteenth century, most ordinary people in England were wearing at least woollen socks which offered both warmth and comfort. By 1841 the *London Magazine of Domestic Economy* was recommending the wearing of three pairs of socks during the winter months.

By the time of World War One, the sock had become the prized possession of Tommies on the Western Front. Trench Foot, a condition brought on by the persistence of wet and cold feet, was a pervasive problem for soldiers. The best way to combat the problem was the regular drying of feet and changing of socks. Comfort Committees sprang up across the Allied nations to knit socks for the brothers and sons of muddy Flanders. In Australia, for example, over 1.2 million pairs of socks were hand knitted and sent off to soldiers.

By the 1920s Argyle socks had become the height of fashion for men in England. Still common today, these socks had a coloured diamond pattern and

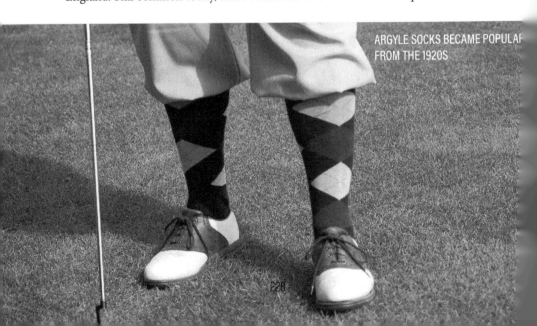

ARGYLE SOCKS BECAME POPULAR FROM THE 1920S

became particularly associated with golf, when men would match them with their knickerbockers.

A revolution in sock making occurred in 1938 with the invention of nylon, which catered both to men's socks and women's tights. The elasticity of nylon kept socks tight on the leg without slipping, a problem which had been confounding hosiers for centuries. An advertisement in the *Daily Gazette* in December 1939 read, 'Men's socks, pure wool, new elastic garter tops. In fancy patterns. Pre-war price.'

Once it became socially acceptable for women to wear trousers in the 1960s, the sock became democratised as an item of apparel for everyone.

UMA THURMAN IN *PULP FICTION* (MIRAMAX, 1994)

39
THE DRINKING STRAW

One of the most memorable scenes in Quentin Tarantino's 1994 cult classic *Pulp Fiction* is when Uma Thurman's character orders the mysterious '$5 Milkshake' at a diner. John Travolta, curious about how a milkshake could possibly be so expensive, leans over to try it. 'You can use my straw. I don't have cooties,' says Thurman. He takes her straw and tastes it. 'God damn, that's a pretty fucking good milkshake.'

The milkshake, and by extension the straw, are American cultural icons. From the teenagers in *Grease* to Mariel Hemingway in Woody Allen's *Manhattan*, using a drinking straw reflects a childlike innocence in some contexts, while in others it can be suggestive and even overtly sexual. In the 2011 movie *Crazy Stupid Love*, Steve Carell's character, struggling with reclaiming his sense of male identity, is downing a vodka and cranberry using a straw. Ryan Gosling's character interrupts him with the quip, 'Would you take that straw out of your mouth please? It looks like you're sucking on a tiny schwanz'. Gosling's character is revealing the hostility some men have for drinking straws; that they are the preserve of women and that it is emasculating for men to use them. In fact, bar workers will sometimes include a straw in a woman's cocktail, but not a man's. This is for two reasons. Firstly, lipstick marks on glasses are notoriously difficult to clean. A straw sorts that issue. Secondly, men will often simply discard the straw and then it is wasted.

It is estimated that 200 million straws are used in the US alone each day. More and more bars and restaurants are now moving to the more sustainable model of paper straws. In many ways we have come full circle with straw manufacturing. When the modern drinking straw was invented in the 1880s by Washington DC native Martin Stone, it was made from manila paper as 'a cheap, durable, and unobjectionable' alternative to the ryegrass straws that were popular at the time. He hated the grassy flavour the straw gave his favoured cocktail, the mint julep. It disintegrated easily, leaving a residue in the liquid.

'Stone fashioned his first straw by winding strips of paper around a pencil, removing the pencil, and gluing the strips together. This improved device was test-marketed at a local drinking establishment and enthusiastically received', according to Chris Broda-Bahm at the *Smithsonian*. He then added paraffin wax to the straw to make it more durable. He had a factory which specialised in making holders for cylindrical objects, such as cigarette cases. An 1899 advertisement for Stone's Patent Paper Julep Straws described the product as being 'entirely free from TASTE or ODOR'. Soon they were being adopted in soda fountains, the bars cropping up across the country serving all manner of sweet fizzy drinks and ice cream floats.

The drinking straw may have gained widespread popularity at the turn of the twentieth century but as an invention it is, in fact, an ancient one. The earliest evidence of the straw goes all the way back to the Sumerians, almost 5,000 years ago. Sumeria, which was a part of Mesopotamia, was the world's earliest civilisation. It was located in what we would today describe as southern Iraq. Beer was a major part of their economy. 'In Sumeria, beer was rarely clarified but rather drunk directly from the brewing vat', according to the writers of *Bread, Beer and the Seeds of Change*. 'Since considerable solid material would be floating

▲ CYLINDER SEAL ILLUSTRATING DRINKING STRAWS, 3600 BC. BRITISH MUSEUM

in the brew, particularly hulls from the grain, Sumerians drank from the bottom of the vat using "straws". Sumerians would gather around a large vat and drink communally, each with their own straw dipped in the barrel. A metre-long gold straw, dating from 2450 BC, makes part of the Middle East collection in Penn Museum, Philadelphia. This was discovered during excavation of the tomb of Queen Puabi in Ur (a city in Sumeria). Sumerian straws were exceptionally long to allow the user to reach into a deep barrel. They were sometimes sealed at the end with small perforations which acted as a filtering system. Although commoners in Sumerian society would have used natural reed straws, the use of precious metals was a way for the aristocracy to show their elevated status.

In modern history the natural reed or ryegrass straw permeated consumer culture until Martin Stone introduced his paper alternative. With this invention, Stone ignited a major new industry. In the first quarter of the twentieth century straw production increased at an almost unbelievable pace. One hundred and sixty-five million straws were manufactured in 1901 in America alone. By 1924 there were four billion being produced annually. 'To people living through the early twentieth century, the straw was a creation of the new public-health regime,' argues Alexis Madrigal in the *Atlantic* magazine. The straw was seen as a more hygienic way of drinking, in a time when disease was more widespread than it is today. Society's increasing obsession with cleanliness even led to the development of the straw dispenser, so that only the user, and not the server, touched them. An advertisement for one such dispenser in the *Practical Soda Fountain Guide* from 1911 says, 'Protects straws from flies, dust and microbes. Positively dispenses one straw at a time'.

The bendy straw came into existence during the 1940s. Joseph Friedman, an inventor based in San Francisco, was in his brother's soda fountain parlour one day when he observed his daughter struggling to drink through a regular straw. She wasn't tall enough to reach the top of it, so he started to develop a straw which could bend at an angle. He inserted a screw into the top of a regular paper straw and then wound dental floss around the indentations of the screw to create an accordion-like effect that would allow it to easily bend. Initially he set up the Flexible Straw Corporation, later renaming it the Flex-Straw Company. Hospitals took great interest in his invention because it allowed patients who were lying down in bed to drink liquid without having to be completely upright. An early advert for his bendy straw shows some very happy sick people using his new invention, claiming that it 'accommodates to any position – no other drinking tube has this feature. Eliminates danger of breakage when used by children,

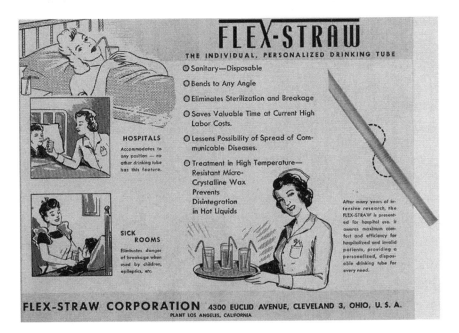

▲ JOSEPH FRIEDMAN'S BENDY STRAW

epileptics, etc.' In 1969 he sold his company and the new owners soon replaced paper with plastic, becoming one of the largest producers of plastic straws in America.

Plastic straws were cheaper to produce and didn't disintegrate in liquid. Environmental concerns were not on the agenda at that time and so the plastic straw became king. But the king's time appears to be up. More and more food and beverage outlets, from McDonald's to Starbucks, are phasing out plastic straws. As the paper straw sees a renaissance, one can only imagine the smile on Martin Stone's face when he first thought up the idea while sipping on a cool mint julep back in 1888.

▲ PATERNOSTER LIFT IN THE CITY HALL IN STUTTGART, GERMANY

THE LIFT

In Stephen King's *The Shining*, the hotel's old creaking lift operates almost like an extra character in the book. The screech and haunting moans of its internal mechanics add a frightful score in the reader's mind to the terror unfolding in the hotel.

'Wendy had a true claustrophobe's horror of the elevator,' writes King. 'She envisioned the three of them trapped in it between floors while the winter storms raged outside, she could see them growing thinner and weaker, starving to death. Or perhaps dining on each other.' King's sense of the macabre aside, the elevator operates much like airplanes do in the public imagination. People either don't think twice about them, or else have nightmares about getting into them. But what are the origins of this sense of terror? When it first launched in the mid-nineteenth century it was like a miracle. How could such a thing defy gravity? This sense of mystery, added to the reports of fatal accidents with early elevators, inspired a mythology that persists to this day.

In 1862 the *New York Times* reported on a fatal elevator accident. 'Henry Lendoff, a German, residing at No.162 Howard Street, was killed on Wednesday, by the accidental falling of an elevator ... The fastenings of the elevator, with a heavy load upon it, gave way at the fifth storey, and fell with a great crash. In the downfall, the deceased was crushed in a horrible manner.' With reports like this, people were naturally fearful of lifts in the mid-nineteenth century, as engineers attempted to find a safe means of installing early elevator technologies.

New Yorker Elisha Graves Otis had invented an elevator in 1853, but after

seven months he had only received one order. He brought his contraption to
the Exhibition of Industry of All Nations in New York to demonstrate not only
its effectiveness but also his new safety mechanism. 'He installed a platform on
guide rails on which he had himself hoisted into the air before the onlookers,'
according to Andreas Bernard in *Lifted: A Cultural History of the Elevator*.
'When the platform had risen to its maximum height, to their horror, he severed
its suspension cable.' Rather than plunging to a grisly death, Otis's new safety
mechanism kicked in, locking the platform into projecting teeth which held
the elevator in place. This important safety device eventually had an enormous
impact on reassuring the public about the safety of elevators and paved the way
for their gradual introduction over the following decades.

Otis installed the world's first passenger elevator in the five storey E.V.
Haughwout Building in Manhattan, in 1857. It featured his trademark safety catch
mechanism and was powered by a steam engine using belts and shafts to elevate
a moving cabin. It cost $300 (about $9,000 in today's money) and moved at 40
feet per minute (today's fastest elevator is housed in the Shanghai Tower in China
and travels at 67 feet per *second*). Historian Amanda Foreman says that visitors to
America in the 1850s and '60s were astounded by the new technology. 'There's a
story of the Duke of Devonshire, who went to New York and he tried an elevator
and then he wrote home to his family to say, "I just rode on a vertical railroad".'

In 1859 the first hotel elevator was installed in the Fifth Avenue Hotel in
Manhattan. This was a 'screw elevator,' run, once again, on steam. It was invented
by Boston native Otis Tufts. This consisted of an enormous screw-type structure
which ran up the middle of the lift shaft. The elevator then wound itself around
the screw, causing it to move upwards.

In his biography of Hitler, Ian Kershaw describes the Chancellor's foreign
relations policy during the mid-1930s. He quotes the Führer as saying, 'When it
comes, seize the opportunity. Get into the paternoster lift at the right time. But
also get out again at the right time'. It comes as no surprise that Hitler would use
the Paternoster as a metaphor since this type of elevator was extremely popular
in Germany. Liverpudlian architect Peter Ellis invented the Paternoster lift in
1860 with one of the earliest models being installed in the General Post Office in
London in 1876. It consists of multiple two-person cabins moving in an endless
loop. There are no doors on the cars, meaning that passengers must embark

and alight while the elevator continues to move. One of the attractions of this system is that you don't have to wait so long for the next elevator to arrive. On the other hand, the notion of a lift that doesn't stop is terrifying to some, feeding into the well-established culture of anxiety that lifts can engender in people.

'Paternoster' is Latin for 'our father', drawing a parallel between the way the religious move rosary beads continuously through their hands, just as the elevator glides continuously through its shaft. One of the most famous examples is the

▲ PATERNOSTER LIFT

paternoster in Stuttgart Town Hall, in operation since 1956. The paternoster in the Springer premises in Berlin has 36 cabins covering 20 floors. There are over 200 paternoster lifts still operating in Germany today.

It is no coincidence that the elevator came into its own at the same time as the emergence of tower blocks and eventually the skyscraper in the late nineteenth century. The arrival of steel and concrete helped buildings to get increasingly tall, but they would have been impractical without the simultaneous development of elevator technology. Who wants to walk up 20 flights of stairs?

The introduction of hydraulic power allowed the elevator to reach ever greater heights. 'The advent of the hydraulic elevator could propel a fully loaded elevator car at 600 to 800 feet per minute, far quicker than the antiquated steam type,' writes Joseph Korom in *The American Skyscraper*. This type of elevator was first pioneered in the 1860s in England, based on the system of hydraulics developed by engineer William Armstrong. The hydraulic elevator operates on Pascal's

Principle. Fluid is pumped between
a reservoir and a cylinder under the
lift. As the fluid enters the cylinder it
pushes a piston upwards, lifting the
elevator to the top of the shaft. When
a valve is opened, the fluid returns to
the reservoir and the elevator lowers.
These elevators first gained ground in
England, France and Germany, before
becoming increasingly popular in the
United States from 1870. 'The piston
had to be long enough to transport
the car to the top floor of the building.
Its limitations were defined by
buildings taller than about twenty
floors,' according to Korom. Although
they were a step forward, they were
problematic. 'Further disadvantages
of this system included frozen water
pipes ... leaking valves or cylinders ...
Occasionally the passenger car crept
away from its landing, forcing riders
to step up or down to their desired
floor.'

Unlike modern steel elevators, the
lifts at the end of the nineteenth and
beginning of the twentieth centuries
were beautiful and decorative
structures, made of mahogany, cherry
or oak. In Lee Edward Grey's *From
Ascending Rooms to Express Elevators*,
he quotes an 1897 catalogue for
elevator car manufacturers L.S Graves
& Son. The description offers a unique

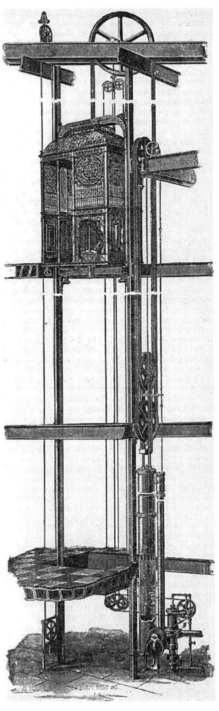

▲ OTIS STANDARD HYDRAULIC PASSENGER
LIFT, 1911

insight into the style and elegance of hydraulic elevators at that time. These were not merely cranes to lug people from one floor to another. Rather, they were comfortable spaces to be enjoyed. 'The interior fittings – seats, mirror, plate or stained glass, chandeliers etc. – should harmonize with the surroundings and business. We make most of our settees with upholstered seats and back, covered with the best prepared leather.' Elevators also offered women an opportunity to adjust their makeup. 'Mirrors, either plain or beveled, are quite ornamental and useful, especially in cars much used by ladies,' reads the catalogue.

Werner von Siemens, the founder of the German appliances giant, invented the world's first electric lift in 1880. He demonstrated it at an exhibition in Mannheim, bringing guests to the top of a 20-metre observation tower. Electricity was slow to take hold in this area of technology because the hydraulic system still reigned supreme. However, it soon became apparent that there were enormous benefits to its application. Hydraulic lifts required a lot of space, with the pistons being dug very deep into the ground. 'Once the acceleration and safety problems of the earliest electric machines were solved by the early 1890s, the most important arguments for their introduction were their inexpensive operation and ease of installation in existing buildings,' explains Bernard. However, it was the launch of the Gearless Electric Traction Elevator, by the Otis Elevator Company in 1902, that set the new standard for lift technology and helped electricity to leapfrog hydraulic systems.

Elevator operators became mandatory in Berlin in 1893. Hydraulic lifts and early electric lifts had to be driven and controlled with great caution. German operators underwent training and were expected to take full responsibility for the riders in their care. 'On the one hand, he had to stop the cab just as it reached the intended landing, on the other, in hydraulic elevators, he also had to regulate the speed by closing or opening a valve between the water line and the piston by means of a control cable or a hand wheel,' explains Bernard. Right up to the 1960s, and beyond, the operator played an important role in manual lifts, before the introduction of automation. In fact, the elevator in *The Shining* is manual. King writes, 'As the number 2 rose on the shaft wall, he threw the brass handle back to the home position and the elevator car creaked to a stop'.

In the TV series *Mad Men,* Don Draper often interacts with colleagues in the office elevator, a brilliantly useful device for writers who want to pit conflicting characters against each other in a tight space from which they can't immediately escape. The elevator operator Hollis, played by La Monde Byrd, chit chats with Don on his arrival and exit from the car, adding to the rich colour that the series paints of mid-twentieth century office culture, not to mention the racial divide in the workplace.

In 1931 the Empire State Building became the first building in the world to have over 100 floors. Otis was contracted to supply 70 elevators for this icon of Art Deco architecture. The company continues to be a market leader today, supplying elevators for the world's tallest building, the Burj Khalifa, in the late 2000s.

▲ THE ELEVATOR LOBBY IN THE EMPIRE STATE BUILDING

Leabharlanna Poiblí Chathair Baile Átha Cliath

Sources

CPI Inflation Calculator: http://www.
in2013dollars.com

Early Office Museum

Online Etymology Dictionary: https://www.
etymonline.com/

Palais Musee de la Mode

Royal Museums Greenwich

Sterling Inflation Calculator: https://www.
bankofengland.co.uk/monetary-policy/
inflation/inflation-calculator

The British Newspaper Archive

The Irish Newspaper Archive

The Irish Times Archive

The Museum of London

The New York Times Archive

The Science Museum, London

The Smithsonian National Museum of American
History

The Victoria & Albert Museum, London

The Wellcome Collection, London

US Inflation Calculator: www.
usinflationcalculator.com

Bibliography

Bailey, Jacqui: Abortion, Rosen Central, 2011,
pg.23

Bannon, Aoife: Richard Branson: Ireland has
come a long way since I was fined for selling
condoms, The Sun, 26/11/15, https://www.
thesun.ie/archives/irish-news/107832/
richard-branson-ireland-has-come-a-long-
way-since-i-was-fined-for-selling-condoms/,
Date of access: 05/19

Barker Kathleen: Dishwashing machine. In
Welch, R., Lamphier, P (Eds): Technical
Innovation in American History: An
Encyclopedia of Science and Technology, Vol.
1, ABC-CLIO, 2019, p.48-49

Baynes, Chris: Hubert Cecil Booth: British
Engineer Revolutionised Cleaning By
Sucking Up Dust With His Mouth, The
Independent, 03/07/18, https://www.
independent.co.uk/life-style/gadgets-and-
tech/news/hubert-cecil-booth-vacuum-
cleaner-inventor-google-doodle-sucking-up-
dust-mouth-a8429811.html, Date of access:
06/19

Bayot, Jennifer: George Atkinson Dies at 69;
Pioneer in Renting of Videos, New York
Times, 09/03/05, https://www.nytimes.
com/2005/03/09/business/media/george-
atkinson-dies-at-69-pioneer-in-renting-of-
videos.html, Date of access: 05/19

Bir, Sara: From Poison to Passion: The

Secret History of the Tomato, Modern
Farmer, 02/09/14, https://modernfarmer.
com/2014/09/poison-pleasure-secret-history-
tomato/, Date of access: 06/19

Brandt, Allen: The Cigarette Century: The Rise,
Fall, and Deadly Persistence of the Product
That Defined America, Basic Books, 2009

Briggs, Paula & Kovacs, Gabor: Contraception:
A Casebook from Menarche to Menopause,
Cambridge University Press, 2013

Briggs, Paula & Kovacs, Gabor: Contraception:
A Casebook from Menarche to Menopause,
Cambridge University Press, 2013

Broda-Bahn, Chris: The Straight Truth About
the Flexible Drinking Straw, 01/06/02,
The Smithsonian, https://invention.si.edu/
straight-truth-about-flexible-drinking-straw,
Date of access: 06/19

Brownlee, John: How 500 Years Of Weird
Condiment History Designed The Heinz
Ketchup Bottle, Fast Company, 21.12.13,
https://www.fastcompany.com/1673352/
how-500-years-of-weird-condiment-history-
designed-the-heinz-ketchup-bottle, Date of
access: 05/19

Brox, Jane: Brilliant: The Evolution of Artificial
Light, Souvenir Press, 2011

Bullock, TK. & Tonkin, MB: The Wigmaker
in Eighteenth-Century Williamsburg: An
Account of his Barbering, Hair-dressing, &
Peruke-Making Services, & some Remarks
on Wigs of Various Styles, Library Of
Alexandria, 2019, pg.21-22

Burch, Druin: Digging Up the Dead: Uncovering
the Life and Times of an Extraordinary
Surgeon, Vintage, 2007

Candappa, Rohan: Picklehead: From Ceylon
to suburbia; a memoir of food, family and
finding yourself, Ebury Press, 2007, pg. 243

Carcopino, Jerome: Daily Life in Ancient Rome
- The People and the City at the Height of the
Empire, Carcopino Press, 2011

Casanova, Giacomo: The Complete Memoirs
of Jacques Casanova de Seingalt, Library of
Alexandria, 2003

Cockburn, Thomas Aidan & Cockburn, Eve &
Reyman, Theodore A: Mummies, Disease
and Ancient Cultures, Cambridge University
Press, 1998

Cole, Shaun: The Story of Men's Underwear,
Parkstone International, 2018

Collins, Liam, Press rewind to view the heyday
of a video empire, The Irish Independent,
31/01/16, https://www.independent.ie/
business/irish/press-rewind-to-view-the-
heyday-of-a-video-empire-34410206.html,
Date of access: 06/19

Connolly, Kate: Lovin' their elevator: why Germans are loopy about their revolving lifts, The Guardian, 14/08/15, https://www.theguardian.com/world/2015/aug/14/elevator-germans-loopy-revolving-lifts-paternosters, Date of access: 06/19

Coryate, Thomas: Coryat's Crudities: Hastily gobled up in Five Moneth's Travels, 1611

Cosmetics and Personal Care Products in the Medicine and Science Collections, Smithsonian National Museum of American History, https://www.si.edu/spotlight/health-hygiene-and-beauty/oral-care, Date of access: 05/19

Cumo, Christopher: Foods that Changed History: How Foods Shaped Civilization from the Ancient World to the Present, ABC-CLIO, 2015

Cunnington, C. Willett: The History of Underclothes, Dover Publications Inc, 2000

Currie, Elizabeth: A Cultural History of Dress and Fashion in the Renaissance, Bloomsbury Visual Arts, 2018

Cutler, Tom: Slap and Tickle: The Unusual History of Sex and the People Who Have it, Constable, 2012

Daniell, Christopher: Death and Burial in Medieval England 1066-1550, Routledge, 1997

DiBacco, Thomas V: Made in the U.S.A: The History of American Business, Beard Books, 2003, p.206-207

Dickson, Del: The People's Government: An Introduction to Democracy, Cambridge University Press, 2014, p.176

Dos Passos, John: The Best Times: An Informal Memoir, Open Road Distribution, 2015

Ellis, Markman & Coulton, Richard & Mauger, Matthew: Empire of Tea: The Asian Leaf that Conquered the World, Reaktion Books, 2015

Everts, Sarah, How Advertisers Convinced Americans They Smelled Bad, The Smithsonian, 02/08/12, https://www.smithsonianmag.com/history/how-advertisers-convinced-americans-they-smelled-bad-12552404/, Date of access: 06/19

Ewbank, Anne: Toasting Your Friends Once Involved Actual Toast, Atlas Obscura, 26/12/18, https://www.atlasobscura.com/articles/toasting-drinking-toast-bread-origin, Date of access: 06/19

Fanebust, Wayne: The Missing Corpse: Grave Robbing a Gilded Age Tycoon, Praeger, 2005, p. 67

Faulk, Richard: The Next Big Thing: A History of the Boom-or-Bust Moments That Shaped the Modern World, Zest Books, 2015

Fink, Johannes Karl: Materials, Chemicals and Methods for Dental Applications, Wiley-Scrivener, 2018

Fisher, MH (Ed): The Travels of Dean Mahomet: An Eighteenth-Century Journey through India, University of California Press, 1997

Foreman, Katya: Converse Shoes: In the all star game, 21/10/14, http://www.bbc.com/culture/story/20140606-art-on-canvas-converse-shoes, Date of access: 06/19

Foss, Richard: Food in the Air and Space: The Surprising History of Food and Drink in the Skies, Rowman & Littlefield Publishers, 2014

Foster, Craig L & Watson, Marianne T: American Polygamy: A History of Fundamentalist Mormon Faith, The History Press, 2019

Foulkes, Debbie: JOSEPHINE COCHRANE (1839-1913) Invented the Dishwasher, 20/04/10, https://forgottennewsmakers.com/2010/04/20/josephine-cochrane-1839-1913-invented-the-dishwasher/, Date of access: 05/19

Fox, Barry: Patent Place, New Scientist, December 22-29, 1983

Freeberg, Ernest: The Age of Edison: Electric Light and the Invention of Modern America, Penguin, 2013

Freeman, Mike: Clarence Saunders and the Founding of Piggly Wiggly: The Rise & Fall of a Memphis Maverick, The History Press, 2011

Fulton, April: A Bumpy Ride: Airplane Food Through The Decades, NPR, 25/09/14, https://www.npr.org/sections/thesalt/2014/09/25/350822871/a-bumpy-ride-airplane-food-through-the-decades, Date of access: 06/19

Funderburg, Anne Cooper: Sundae Best: A History of Soda Fountains, University of Wisconsin Press, 2001

Gantz, Carroll: The Vacuum Cleaner: A History, McFarland, 2012

Garber, Megan, Tower of Light: When Electricity Was New, People Used It to Mimic the Moon, The Atlantic, 06/03/13, https://www.theatlantic.com/technology/archive/2013/03/tower-of-light-when-electricity-was-new-people-used-it-to-mimic-the-moon/273445/, Date of access: 06/19

Goldsmith, Sara: The Rise of the Fork, Slate, 20/06/12, http://www.slate.com/articles/arts/design/2012/06/the_history_of_the_fork_when_we_started_using_forks_and_how_their_design_changed_over_time_.html, Date of access: 07/19

Goodman, Ruth: The Victorian Condom, The Atlantic, 12/14, https://www.theatlantic.com/magazine/archive/2014/12/vsbecondoms/382245/, Date of access: 05/19

Grahn, Emma & Kearney, Caitlin: Tasting the 1930s: An experiment with congealed salads and other one-dish wonders, National Museum of American History, 16/11/15, https://americanhistory.si.edu/blog/tasting-1930s-experiment-congealed-salads-and-other-one-dish-wonders, Date of access: 06/19

Greenberg, Joshua M: From Betamax to Blockbuster: Mediation in the Consumption Junction, Cornell University, 2004

Greenberg, Joshua M: From Betamax to Blockbuster: Video Stores and the Invention of Movies on Video, MIT Press, 2010

Gretton, Lel: http://www.oldandinteresting.com/antique-irons-smoothers-mangles.aspx, Date of access: 05/19

Gretton, Lel: http://www.oldandinteresting.com/fluting-goffering-irons.aspx, Date of access: 05/19

Gross, Linda: The History of Making Toast, Hagley Museum and Library, 19/06/17, https://www.hagley.org/librarynews/history-making-toast, Date of access: 05/19

Guizzi, Giulio: Cleaning and sanitation: a global history, Edizioni LSWR, 2016

Gwynn, Mary: Back In Time For Dinner: From Spam to Sushi: How We've Changed the Way We Eat, Transworld Digital, 2015

Halime, Farah: The Martha Stewart of a.d. 800 was an Arabic Dude, OZY, 01/09/15, https://www.ozy.com/flashback/the-martha-stewart-of-ad-800-was-an-arabic-dude/62166, Date of access: 05/19

Handley, Sasha: Sleep in Early Modern England, Yale University Press, 2016

Harrison, Rosina: The Lady's Maid: My Life in Service, Ebury, 2011, p.11

Haynes, Joseph R: Virginia Barbecue: A History, The History Press, 2016

Hayward, Maria: Luxury in English and Scottish Sumptuary Law. In Riello, Georgio & Rublack, Ulinka (Eds): The Right to Dress: Sumptuary Laws in a Global Perspective, c.1200–1800, Cambridge University Press, 2019, pg.116

Heffernan, Virginia: Against Headphones, New York Times, 07/01/11, https://www.nytimes.com/2011/01/09/magazine/09FOB-medium-t.html, Date of access: 06/19

Henderson, William Otto: The Genesis of the Common Market, Routledge, 1985, p.8

Henesy, Declan: Tine After Tine: An Early History of the Fork, Seconds Food History, https://www.secondshistory.com/home/2019/3/22/tine-after-tine-an-early-history-of-the-fork, Date of access: 05/19

Hickox, Rex: All You Wanted to Know about 18th Century Royal Navy, Rex Publishing, 2005, pg.19-20

Hilpern, Kate: The Secret History of the Dishwasher, The Independent, 29/10/10, https://www.independent.co.uk/life-style/gadgets-and-tech/features/the-secret-history-of-the-dishwasher-2119320.html, Date of access: 06/19

Hilton, Lisa: Elizabeth: Renaissance Prince, Weidenfeld & Nicolson, 2014

Hindley, Meredith: Glamorous Crossing: How Pan Am Airways Dominated International Travel in the 1930s, Longreads, 2015, https://longreads.com/2015/02/10/glamorous-crossing-how-pan-am-airways-dominated-international-travel-in-the-1930s/, Date of access: 05/19

Hirsch, Michele Lent: Ride This Bizarre, Old-School Elevator Before They All Shut Down, The Smithsonian, 04/06/15, https://www.smithsonianmag.com/travel/ride-bizarre-old-school-elevator-they-all-shut-down-180955461/, Date of access: 06/19

Hirst, Chris: Has fast-food culture turned a British staple into an agent of poisoning?, The Independent, 07/10/04, https://www.independent.co.uk/life-style/health-and-families/health-news/lettuce-5351147.html, Date of access: 05/19

How Elevators Changed the World | Origins: The Journey of Humankind, National Geographic, https://www.youtube.com/watch?v=UtkAJscxbZU, Date of access: 05/19

http://tobaccopipeartistory.blogspot.com/2013/03/sir-walter-raleighs-pipe.html

http://www.asharperrazor.com/tutorials/brief-history-of-the-straight-razor, Date of access: 06/19

http://www.bordbiavantage.ie/market-information/sector-overviews/chilled-food/, Date of access: 05/19

http://www.defenderofjerusalem.com/richard-i-and-the-third-crusade.html, Date of access: 06/19

http://www.flemming-hamburg.de/patlist.htm#deutschland, Date of access: 05/06/19

http://www.palaisgalliera.paris.fr/en/work/marius-system-umbrella, Date of access: 06/19

http://www.todayifoundout.com/index.php/2016/05/bureaucratic-obstacles-referred-red-tape/, Date of access: 06/19

https://artsandculture.google.com/asset/thor-electric-washing-machine-circa-1907/ygHvPsX_aU9gTg, Date of access: 05/19 https://darbymade.com/blogs/journal/jean-marius, Date of access: 05/19

https://www.eater.com/2014/8/21/6214423/the-strange-history-of-frozen-food-from-clarence-birdseye-to-the, Eater, 21/08/14, Date of access: 05/19

https://www.firstversions.com/2015/07/hoover-vacuum-cleaners.html, Date of access: 05/19

https://www.history.com/this-day-in-history/ireland-allows-sale-of-contraceptives, Date of access: 05/19

https://www.independentpharmacist.co.uk/shampoo-taking-the-sting-out-of-childhood, Date of access: 06/19

https://www.lookandlearn.com/blog/23616/hanways-umbrella-gave-protection-in-the-wet-british-weather/, Date of access: 05/19

https://www.officemuseum.com/stapler_gallery_magazine.htm, Date of access: 05/19

https://www.ourheritageofhealth.com/victorian-shampoo-alternatives/, Date of access: 06/19

https://www.ucl.ac.uk/museums-static/digitalegypt/burialcustoms/coffinsok.html, Date of access: 05/19

Huang, H.T: Fermentations and Food Science. In Needham, Joseph: Science and Civilisation in China: Volume 6, Biology and Biological Technology, Cambridge University Press, 2001, pg.398

Hug, Chrystel: The Politics of Sexual Morality in Ireland, Macmillan Press Ireland, 1998, pg.122-124

Hutchinson, Alex: Big Ideas: 100 Modern Inventions That Have Transformed Our World, Sterling Publishing Co Inc., 2009

Iacocca, Lee & Novak, William: Iacocca: An Autobiography , Bantam, 2007, p.313

Jack, Albert: Food History & Recipe Origins: The Origins of the Names of the World's Favorite Recipes, Albert Jack Publishing, 2014

Jackson, Lee: Dirty Old London: The Victorian Fight Against Filth, Yale University Press, 2014, pg. 164-165

Jackson, Nicholas: Mousetraps: A Symbol of the American Entrepreneurial Spirit, The Atlantic, 28/03/11, https://www.theatlantic.com/technology/archive/2011/03/mousetraps-a-symbol-of-the-american-entrepreneurial-spirit/70573/, Date of access: 06/19

James, Wayne: Manly Manners: Lifestyle & Modern Etiquette for the Young Man of the 21St Century, iUniverse, 2016

Jango-Cohen, Judith: The History of Food, Twenty First Century Books, 2001, pg. 28

Journal of the History of Dentistry: Official Publication of the American Academy of the History of Dentistry, Volumes 50-51, pg. 75

Jurafsky, Dan: The Language of Food: A Linguist Reads the Menu, W. W. Norton & Company, 2014

Jurgensen, John: Going Up? Elevator Scenes on 'Mad Men', The Wall Street Journal, 26/04/15, https://www.wsj.com/articles/what-floor-elevator-scenes-on-mad-men-1427304646, Date of access: 06/19

Jütte, Robert: Contraception: A History, Polity Press, 2008

Karch, Steven B: A Brief History of Cocaine, CRC Press, 2005

Kearns, Kevin C: Dublin Street Life and Lore – An Oral History of Dublin's Streets and their Inhabitants: The Recollections of Dublin's Tram Drivers, Lamplighters and Street Dealers, Gill & Macmillan, 1997

Kern, Kevin F & Wilson, Gregory S: Ohio: A History of the Buckeye State, John Wiley & Sons, 2014

Kershaw, Ian: Hitler, Penguin, 2013, p.vii

Keyser, AJ: Sneaker Century: A History of Athletic Shoes, Twenty-First Century Books, 2015

King, Seth S: Lighting a Fire in the Barbecue Business, New York Times, 03/0777, https://www.nytimes.com/1977/07/03/archives/lighting-a-fire-in-the-barbecue-business.html, Date of access: 06/19

King, Stephen: The Shining, Hodder & Stoughton, 1977

Knowlden, Margaret: Strike Before the Iron is Hot, Little Red Apple Publishing, 2001

Knowles, John: How Sex Got Screwed Up: The Ghosts that Haunt Our Sexual Pleasure - Book Two: From Victoria to Our Own Times, Vernon Press, 2018, pg.227

König, Anna: Umbrellas and Parasols, https://fashion-history.lovetoknow.com/fashion-accessories/umbrellas-parasols, Date of access: 05/19

Korkki, Phyllis: The Attachment That Still Makes Noise, New York Times, 23/03/13, https://www.nytimes.com/2013/03/24/business/staplers-the-attachment-thats-still-making-noise.html?login=smartlock&auth=login-smartlock, Date of access: 05/19

Koslofsky, Craig: Evening's Empire: A History of the Night in Early Modern Europe, Cambridge University Press, 2013

Krafchik, B, History of diapers and diapering, International Journal of Dermatology, 55 (Suppl. 1): 4–6, 2016

Laskow, Sarah, The Woman Who Invented Disposable Diapers, 14/10/14, The Atlantic,https://www.theatlantic.com/

technology/archive/2014/10/the-woman-who-invented-disposable-diapers/381310/, Date of access: 05/19

Lazenby, Roland: Michael Jordan: The Life, Little, Brown and Company, 2014

Lead cremation vessels and coffins, Museum of London, https://www.museumoflondon.org.uk/application/files/7715/2708/7761/Lead_cremation_vessels_and_coffins.pdf, Date of access: 06/19

Licence, Amy: Not such a prude after all: the secrets of Henry VIII's love life, 08/02/16, https://www.historyextra.com/period/tudor/not-such-a-prude-after-all-the-secrets-of-henry-viiis-love-life/, Date of access: 07/19

Licence, Amy: In Bed with the Tudors: The Sex Lives of a Dynasty from Elizabeth of York to Elizabeth I, Amberley Publishing, 2012

Licence, Amy: The Six Wives & Many Mistresses of Henry VIII: The Women's Stories, Amberley Publishing, 2014

Life Magazine, 05/05/52, p.172

Mantle, Jonathan: Companies That Changed the World: From the East India Company to Google Inc., Quercus, 2014

Mariani, John & Mariani, Galina: The Italian American Cookbook: A Feast of Food from a Great American Cooking Tradition, Harvard Common Press, 2001

Markides, CC & Geroski, PA: Fast Second: How Smart Companies Bypass Radical Innovation to Enter and Dominate New Markets, Jossey-Bass, 2004, p.94

Marsh, Madeleine: Compacts and Cosmetics: Beauty from Victorian Times to the Present Day, Pen & Sword Military, 2014, p.66

Marshall, Michael L & Taylor, Jerry L: Wicked Kernersville: Rogues, Robbers, Ruffians & Rumrunners, The History Press, 2009

Maxwell, Lee M: Save Women's Lives : History of Washing Machines, Oldewash, 2003

Menocal, Maria Rosa & Sheindlin, Raymond P & Sells, Michael: The Literature of Al-Andalus, Cambridge University Press, 2008, p.64

Merrill, Jane & Endicott, John: Aaron Burr in Exile: A Pariah in Paris, 1810-1811, McFarland & Company Inc, 2016, p.66

Mitchell, Linda Elizabeth: Family Life in the Middle Ages, Greenwood Press, 2007, pg.105

Monroe, Jo: Star of India: The Spicy Adventures of Curry, John Wiley & Sons, 2005, pg.160

Montague, Charlotte, Women of Invention: Life-Changing Ideas by Remarkable Women, Chartwell Books, 2018, p.42

Montague, Charlotte: Women of Invention: Life-Changing Ideas by Remarkable Women, Chartwell Books, 2018, pg.65

Moore, Kenny: Bowerman and the Men of Oregon: The Story of Oregon's Legendary Coach and Nike's Co-founder, Rodale Books, 2007

Moss, Robert F: Barbecue: The History of an American Institution, University of Alabama Press, 2010

Nathan, John: Sony: A Private Life, Houghton Mifflin Company, 1999

Nelson, Megan Kate: A Brief History of the Stoplight, The Smithsonian magazine, May 2018, https://www.smithsonianmag.com/innovation/brief-history-stoplight-180968734/, Date of access: 06/19

Newman, Paul B: Daily Life in the Middle Ages, McFarland and Company, 2001

Newson, Alex: Fifty Sneakers That Changed the World: Design Museum Fifty, Conran Octopus, 2015

Nye, David E: American Illuminations: Urban Lighting, 1800–1920, MIT Press, 2018

O'Keefe, Linda: Shoes: A Celebration of Pumps, Sandals, Slippers & More, Workman Publishing, 1997, pg.383

O'Neil, Darcy S: Fix the Pumps, Art of Drink, 2010

Oatman-Stanford, Hunter: A Brief HIstory of Body Odour, The Week, 27/03/16, https://theweek.com/articles/614722/brief-history-body-odor, Date of access: 05/19

Ohler, Norman: Blitzed: Drugs in Nazi Germany, Penguin, 2016

Okonowicz, Ed: True Crime: Maryland: The State's Most Notorious Criminal Cases, Stackpole Books, 2009, pg.8

Oldstone-Moore, Christopher: Of Beards and Men: The Revealing History of Facial Hair, University of Chicago Press, 2015

Olsen, Kirstin: Daily Life in 18th-century England, Greenwood, 1999

Panati, Charles: Panati's Extraordinary Origins of Everyday Things, Chartwell Books, 2016

Parsons, Frank: The American Stationer, https://americanstationer.wordpress.com/2019/02/01/mcgills-single-stroke-staple-press-no-1/, Date of access: 05/19

Paulson, Ula: 'The Lengberg Castle Bra', https://historicalheadwear.wordpress.com/2016/10/25/the-lengberg-castle-bra/, Date of access: 06/19

Perdew, Laura: How the Toilet Changed History, Essential Library, 2015

Perrot, Michelle & Elkin, Lauren: Bedroom: An Intimate History, Yale University Press, 2018

Peterkin, Allan: One Thousand Beards: A Cultural History of Facial Hair, Arsenal Pulp Press, 2002

Pickup, Gilly: What the British Invented: From the Great to the Downright Bonkers, Amberley Publishing, 2013

Pollan, Michael: The Omnivore's Dilemma: The Search for a Perfect Meal in a Fast-Food World, Bloomsbury Publishing, 2009

Prisco, Jacopo: A short history of the elevator, CNN, 09/02/19, https://edition.cnn.com/style/article/short-history-of-the-elevator/index.html, Date of access: 05/19

Raichlen, Steven: BBQ USA: 425 Fiery Recipes from All Across America, Workman Publishing, 2003

Rance, Caroline: The History of Medicine in 100 Facts, Amberley Publishing, 2015

Rankine, Marion: Brolliology: A History of the Umbrella in Life and Literature, Melville House Publishing, 2017

Ratigan, Dorothy T: Knitting The Perfect Pair: Secrets To Great Socks, Krause Publications, 2009

Rebora, Giovanni: Culture of the Fork: A Brief History of Everyday Food and Haute Cuisine in Europe, Columbia University Press, 2001

Riddle, John M: Contraception and Abortion from the Ancient World to the Renaissance, Harvard University Press, 1994

Ridley, Jaspar: A Brief History of the Tudor Age, Robinson, 2013

Roberts, J.A.G.: China to Chinatown: Chinese Food in the West, Reaktion Books, 2012

Roberts, Michelle: Gerry Thomas, inventor of the TV Dinner, dies at 83, The Seattle Times, 20/07/05, https://www.seattletimes.com/nation-world/gerry-thomas-inventor-of-the-tv-dinner-dies-at-83/, Date of access: 06/19

Robson, Martin: Not Enough Room to Swing a Cat: Naval slang and its everyday usage, Osprey Publishing, 2008

Rosas, Kim: Marion Donovan – Inventor Of The Modern Cloth Diaper, The Boater. 1946, 29/01/15, http://dirtydiaperlaundry.com/marion-donovan-inventor-of-the-modern-cloth-diaper-the-boater-1946/, Date of access: 05/19

Roy, Robin: Consumer Product Innovation and Sustainable Design: The Evolution and Impacts of Successful Products, Routledge, 2016, pg.100

Rupp, Rebecca: Elegantly Dressed Salads Were Once Quite Fashionable, National Geographic, 04/02/15, https://www.nationalgeographic.com/people-and-culture/food/the-plate/2015/02/04//, Date of access: 06/19

Rupp, Rebecca: How Carrots Won the Trojan War: Curious (but True) Stories of Common

Vegetables, Storey Publishing, 2011, p.165-166

Salisbury, Stephan: Penn Museum's Middle East Galleries reopen: Behold, the queen's beer straw, The Philadelphia Inquirer, 19/04/18, https://www.inquirer.com/philly/entertainment/arts/penn-museum-middle-east-galleries-20180419.html, Date of access: 05/19

Saltar, Kate: Cathy Chapman: the woman who changed the way we eat, Daily Telegraph, 10/10/10, https://www.telegraph.co.uk/foodanddrink/8041879/Cathy-Chapman-the-woman-who-changed-the-way-we-eat.html, Date of access: 06/19

Sebesta, Judith Lynn & Bonfante, Larissa: The World of Roman Costume, University of Wisconsin Press, 2006, p.125

Seckerson, Edward: The Pleasure Telephone (documentary), BBC Radio 3, 2011

Semmelhack, Elizabeth: Shoes That Put Women in Their Place, New York Times, 23/05/15, https://www.nytimes.com/2015/05/24/opinion/sunday/shoes-that-put-women-in-their-place.html, Date of access: 05/19

Sharkey, Olive: Old Days, Old Ways: An Illustrated Folk History of Ireland, Syracuse University Press, 1987, p.86

Sherrow, Victoria: Encyclopedia of Hair: A Cultural History, Greenwood Press, 2006

Shmaefsky, Brian: Syphilis, Infobase Publishing, 2003, pg.55

Singman, Jeffrey L: Daily Life in Medieval Europe, Greenwood Press, 1999

Smit, Barbara: Pitch Invasion: Adidas, Puma and the Making of Modern Sport, Penguin, 2007

Smith, Andrew F: Eating History: Thirty Turning Points in the Making of American Cuisine, Columbia University Press, 2009, p.177

Smith, Andrew F: Pure Ketchup: A History of America's National Condiment with Recipes, University of South Carolina Press, 1996

Smith, Andrew F: The Oxford Companion to American Food and Drink, OUP USA, 2007, pg.11

Smith, Bret H: http://www.industrialdesignhistory.com/taxonomy/term/275, Date of access: 15/19

Smith, K Annabelle: Why the Tomato Was Feared in Europe for More Than 200 Years, Smithsonian, 18/06/2013, https://www.smithsonianmag.com/arts-culture/why-the-tomato-was-feared-in-europe-for-more-than-200-years-863735/, Date of access: 06/19

Smith, Peter: The Birth of Non-Alcoholic Ketchup, The Smithsonian, 24/05/12, https://www.smithsonianmag.com/arts-culture/the-birth-of-non-alcoholic-ketchup-104660832/, Date of access: 06/19

Snodgrass, Mary Ellen: World Clothing and Fashion: An Encyclopedia of History, Culture, and Social Influence, Routledge, 2015

Souter, Keith: The Tea Cyclopedia: A Celebration of the World's Favorite Drink, Skyhorse, 2013

Spiegel, Allison: The Caesar Salad Was Invented In Mexico. Surprised?, Huffington Post, 03/11/1515, https://www.huffpost.com/entry/where-was-the-caesar-salad-invented_n_6839542?guccounter=1, Date of access: 05/19

Stamp, Jimmy: A Partial History of Headphones, 19/03/13, https://www.smithsonianmag.com/arts-culture/a-partial-history-of-headphones-4693742, Date of access: 05/19

Stice, Joel: Condom History – From Sheep Intestines To Latex, All That's Interesting, 06/11/17, https://allthatsinteresting.com/history-of-condoms, Date of access: 06/19

Sullum, Jacob: For Your Own Good: The Anti-Smoking Crusade and the Tyranny of Public Health, Simon and Schuster, 1999

Suppel, John: Video Station Sees $10 Mil 1981 Gross, Billboard magazine, 22/11/1980

Suranyi, Anna: The Genius of the English Nation: Travel Writing and National Identity in Early Modern England, University of Delaware Press, 2008, pg.91

The Electrophone – the precursor of pay-for-view, The Telegraph, 25/11/16, https://www.telegraph.co.uk/technology/connecting-britain/electrophone-invention/, Date of access: 05/19

The Spectator, Volume 41, 1868, p. 1091

Thornbury, Walter: Old and New London: Westminster and the western suburbs, Cassell, Petter, & Galpin, 1891

Tjandra, Nathalia: Indonesia's lax smoking laws are helping next generation to get hooked, The Jakarta Post, 04/06/18, https://www.thejakartapost.com/academia/2018/06/04/indonesias-lax-smoking-laws-are-helping-next-generation-to-get-hooked.html, Date of access: 05/19

Tomshinsky, Ida: Socks, 2011

Tully, John: The Devil's Milk: A Social History of Rubber, Monthly Review Press, U.S., 2011, pg.44-45

Victoria & Albert Museum, Tea Tray, 1743, http://collections.vam.ac.uk/item/O21335/tea-tray-unknown/, Date of access: 07/19

von Drachenfels, Suzanne: The Art of the Table, Create Space Independent Publishing Platform, 2013

Waits, Robert K: From Perret to Kampfe: Origins

of the Safety Razor, 2007, http://www.shaveworld.org/images/PerrettKampfe-rev2.html, Date of access: 05/19

Waits, Robert K: Before Gillette: The Quest for a Safe Razor - Inventors and Patents 1762-1901, 2009

Warde, Alan: Consumption, Food and Taste: Culinary Antinomies and Commodity Culture, SAGE Publications Ltd, 1997, pg.152

Wasser, Frederick: Veni, Vidi, Video: The Hollywood Empire and the VCR, University of Texas Press, 2002

Waters, Michael: The Public Shaming of England's First Umbrella User, Atlas Obscura, 27/07/16, https://www.atlasobscura.com/articles/the-public-shaming-of-englands-first-umbrella-user, Date of access: 05/19

Watkins, Julian Lewis: The 100 Greatest Advertisements, Dover, 1959

Weld, Isaac: Travels Through the States of North America, and the Provinces of Upper and Lower Canada, During the Years 1795, 1796, and 1797, Vol. 1, 1799

White, Richard: Smoke Screens: The Truth About Tobacco, lulu.com, 2009

Wiggins, Jasmine: How Was Ketchup Invented, 21/04/14, https://www.nationalgeographic.com/people-and-culture/food/the-plate/2014/04/21/how-was-ketchup-invented/, Date of access: 05/19

Willis, Sam & Daybell, James: Histories of the Unexpected: How Everything Has a History, Atlantic Books, 2018

Wilson, Donald & Wilson, Jane Y: The Pride of African American History, 1st Book Library, 2003, p.139

Winter, James: London's Teeming Streets, 1830-1914, Routledge, 1993p. 34

Winterton, Wayne: Stories from History's Dust Bin, Volume 1, Xlibris US, 2015

Woods, Shaun: Mousetrap Monday, https://mousetrapmonday.com

World Health Organization, Indonesia Tobacco Factsheet 2018

Zarrelli, Natalie: It Was Once Someone's Job to Chat With the King While He Used the Toilet, Atlas Obscura, 06/04/17, https://www.atlasobscura.com/articles/king-toilet-attendant-england, Date of access: 06/19